CLEOPATRA

TRANSLATED BY M. E. POINDEXTER

CLEOPATRA

BY
CLAUDE FERVAL

GARDEN CITY, NEW YORK
GARDEN CITY PUBLISHING CO., INC.

PRINTED IN THE UNITED STATES AT THE COUNTRY LIFE PRESS, GARDEN CITY, N. Y.

FOREWORD

CLEOPATRA, that curiously perverse figure, that incarnation of fatal passion, what was she like? A combination of pride and frailty, adored and despised. Plutarch said that "Her charm entered into men's very souls," and Horace thanked the gods for delivering the earth from that *"Fatale Monstrum."*

It is not the gigantic outlines graven on the dusty walls of the temple at Dendera that will reveal the mystery of Cleopatra; nor yet those bronze medals from Syracuse, with their curious hieratic profiles; disguised by these gross images who would recognize the intelligence, the passion, the daring, the flame, the storm, the witchery, that were united in that "serpent of old Nile"?

If only some masterpiece of Greek sculpture had been preserved! If we possessed that statue made at Cæsar's orders by the sculptor, Timomachus! or that cherished treasure which a rich citizen of Alexandria offered Cæsar Augustus two thousand talents to leave untouched! But all these portraits have disappeared.

Poor as we are in material we can only divine what she really was in appearance and in character. It is not certain that she was beautiful, at least not of that sensuous type of beauty which has been generally attributed to her. But, if tradition which has come down the ages has any weight, with her burning mouth, her radiant eyes, her slender body, which her country's fiery sun had polished till it shone like gilded marble, what creature born of woman was ever more fitted to inspire delight and adoration?

"The kings who crossed her threshold died from excess of love."

But physical beauty alone could not have so ensnared and deprived of reason such warriors as Cæsar and Antony, brave, indefatigable, honourable men, who fell at her feet, forgetting duty, honour, the very memory of their country, for love of her.

We must look further. Her rare intellect, which made her every word of interest; her incomparable, magnetic charm, which banished ennui and held her listeners enthralled; her ardent, passionate nature; these have made her peerless among the fascinators of the world, Circe, Delilah, Heloise, Yseult, Carmen, Sirens or Walkyrie—living women, or creatures of the poets' fancy—all the enchantresses who have driven men to madness have had the one gift in common, that of arousing passion, stirring emotion, fanning the flame of love.

Whether their eyes had the blue of the heavens, or shone like stars at midnight, whether their noses were long or short, their mouths delicate or voluptuous, all the world-heroines have had burning hearts that touched their lovers' hearts with kindred fire.

If Cleopatra stands above all others it is because she possessed in a higher degree that sovereign gift that transforms the dullness of every-day life and creates an atmosphere of rose and gold.

History shows her as crafty, diplomatic, frivolous, generous; capable of horrible cruelties; coveting the whole world; a prey to ambition, yet flinging it all away for the sake of her lover's kiss. But history gives us only half the picture. Its frame is too narrow to hold it all. It is to Imagination and her wingèd daughters, Poetry and Legend, that we have to look for the whole.

The asp with which Shakespeare encircled Cleopatra's arm has made her more famous than her own great plan to wipe out Rome and put Alexandria in its place. The noted sonnet, which shows her in her silver trireme, on the waters of the Cydnus,

> *Dont le sillage laisse un parfum d'encensoir,*
> *Avec les sons de flutes et des frissons de soie.*

shows us more vividly her manner of living, than do all the erudite volumes concerning her life.

Notwithstanding all the splendid efforts to portray her that have been already made, will the Public pardon my attempt to add another taper to light the mysterious ways of that wonderful woman, who, with a lotus flower in her hand, still stands with Antony, weaving the enchanting mists of romance and breathing the warm breath of passion over the crumbling ruins of the world?

CONTENTS

THE LIFE AND DEATH OF CLEOPATRA

I

Julius Cæsar

IT WAS about seven o'clock. On the crowded docks of Alexandria the sailors were unloading the last bales of merchandise. Swiftly, like belated birds, the fishing boats dropped anchor at the old wharves in Eunostus harbour. It was almost dark when the last vessel slipped in stealthily. A man stepped down, broad-shouldered, covered from head to foot with a dark cloak, his traveller's cap pulled down to his ears. With the utmost care he helped a woman to land, a woman so young, so light-footed, that she seemed almost a child.

But, though barely seventeen years of age, would any one have called Cleopatra a child? The wife for two years of the brother, whom the dynastic law had compelled her to marry on the death of her father; cast off by her perfidious consort, sent into exile and, coming back to-night under the care of Apollodorus, she had undoubtedly a store of experience extraordinary for her age. One wonders how her impressions would have compared with those of the average girl, for Cleopatra had grown up in a shamelessly corrupt court and was the daughter of Ptolemy Auletes, that remarkable dilettante king who had met the uproar of revolution and foreign invasion with the persistent playing of his flute.

Descendant of a race cultivated to the last degree, proficient herself in literature and art, with a thorough education, this young girl's outlook on life was one of unusual breadth. At the time when other girls, just released from the women's quarters, still revered virtue and dreamed of pleasure, she had already the inclination to beguile and to rule. With liberal views, she looked things squarely in the face; she fully recognized the value of men, and whether in serving or in pleasing them, had a spirit of rare understanding, keen and comprehensive.

Even in the depths of the Thebaid—whither she had been exiled by the king on the advice of the agitator Photinus—when she heard that Cæsar had arrived in Alexandria, she knew, by that curious intuition of super-sensitive minds, that unexpected good fortune was in store for her. But how could she reach this great man? By what means could she secure from his omnipotence that aid which would transform her from a prisoner to a queen?

It was the Greek savant, Apollodorus, her professor of rhetoric, and warmly attached to her, who opened the negotiations. As Cæsar from the very first interview had shown his interest in behalf of the persecuted young girl rather than in Ptolemy and his crafty minister, Cleopatra had no misgivings. Although she was closely watched and ignorant of the roads, which were infested by gangs of robbers and murderers, she managed to escape with only two slaves for escort, and took passage down the Nile to Canopus, where Apollodorus awaited her. Trusting in his faithful devotion, she was confident of gaining her end.

The voyage, however, was not without danger. In order to escape notice, one of the smallest boats had been selected and the wretched little fishing craft came very near being swallowed up by the waves. Consequently it was with the joy and relief of the rescued voyager that the young Lapida felt the solid ground of her capital under her trembling little feet; that dear Alexandria which by right of birth she looked upon as her own.

The next thing was to gain admission to the palace, and this was by no means easy. In spite of the Roman occupation, soldiers, agents of the Egyptian king, had watchful eyes for all that was going on. If she were recognized Cleopatra would be again in her brother's power.

Fortunately Apollodorus was both ingenious and sturdy. With the exquisite care due such a precious object, he wrapped up the young fugitive and, concealing her in a roll of rugs, hoisted the bundle on his shoulders like an ordinary parcel. Who, seeing this porter walking along the wharf, laden like so many others, would have suspected the mystery hidden in his burden? At the Bruchium he was recognized, but on his declaring that, in response to an order from Cæsar, he was bringing him carpets, the palace guards allowed him to enter.

Julius Cæsar was no longer a young man. All that life could give of glory, power, and pleasure he had had, and at times his nerves showed the effects. Prematurely bald, the deep lines in his face indicated his weariness; but, at the least stimulus the brilliant splendour of his glance shone out. No one could come near the divine Cæsar without immediately recognizing his supremacy; without feeling that magnetic quality of power and charm which could only be explained by remembering his descent by Æneas direct from Venus herself. When he spoke, his gracious gesture, the resonance of his voice, won, at least while he was talking, the sympathy of his listeners. If he were silent, his very silence was eloquent, for people recalled his orations, those memorable words which had made an echo around the world.

Wherever he went, the fame of his astounding deeds surrounded him. Not only was he pictured at the head of his legions, guiding them from one end to the other of that Gaul which he had conquered; not only did the people actually see him, descending on Italy through the terrible ravines of the Alps, crossing at a bound the narrow Rubicon, and sweeping down on Rome in the throes of revolution, which, the instant the conqueror appeared, crouched meekly at his feet; but legend glorified him. The Germans, whom he had defeated, were represented as a race of giants, whose mere glance was death. Britain, where he had been the first to dare set foot, was said to be in total darkness three months of the year and inhabited by spirits. All these fantastic tales added to his real victories made them appear yet more marvellous.

In appealing to a man like this, in coming to him

to seek counsel and help, Cleopatra relied to a certain extent on her natural rights; but she was not so foolish as to believe that being in the right was a woman's surest appeal.

As she got out of the sack, where her charms had been hidden for the past hour, she felt the thrill of a young animal which has just been set free; then, with typical feminine eagerness, she grasped the burnished silver mirror which hung by a chain from her belt. What appalling disorder she beheld! Her dainty overdress was all rumpled; her dishevelled hair fell on her neck in brown waves; of the antimony around her eyes, or the rouge on her lips and cheeks, not a trace was left. But thus simply clad, adorned only with the beauty of youth, was she any less blooming, less expressive, less distracting, this fascinating plaintiff who in a few moments would appear before her judge?

She was anxious, however. She wondered how she would be received by this man who was accustomed to the guile of the Romans, this powerful ruler to whom everyone, the most virtuous as well as the most corrupt, was compelled to yield. For Cæsar's reputation was world-wide, and everyone knew that the great captain, writer, jurist, and orator was a libertine at heart. In addition to those excesses common to all young men, in which he had indulged amidst the gaieties of the world, it was well known that his adventures had brought grief to many households, not excepting those of his best friends; and it was in no kindly spirit that his name was coupled with the phrase: *omnium mulierum vir*—the husband of all women.

Cleopatra, however, was needlessly disturbed. To a temperament craving novelty, originality, fresh experience; to nerves tired as were those of the Emperor, what vision could appeal so intensely as that of this queenly young woman? From the first moment, as he gazed on the rhythmic, harmonious grace of her body; her low, straight brows, the golden light in her eyes; her delicate nostrils, her parted, sensuous lips, her radiant, amber-coloured flesh, suggesting luscious sun-kissed fruit, Cæsar had felt an indescribable thrill run through his veins. Never, no, never before, had the West, or Rome itself, with her ardent virgins, her tempting, seductive matrons, offered him anything so intoxicating. Ready to grant everything that he might attain the height of his desire, he asked: "What can I do for you? What do you seek?"

With charming tact, Cleopatra replied in Latin, which she spoke with the same ease that she did Greek, Egyptian, Syrian, and several other languages. She described the tyranny of which she had been the victim, the criminal injustice which had made her a wanderer, and, with a confiding air which was irresistible, she said that she trusted in the omnipotence of Cæsar to restore her crown.

Her voice was sweet and winning. The things she said, her claims against her usurping brother, became, the moment they left her lips, irrefutable truths. Why should they not have seemed so to the gallant judge, fascinated by the starry light in her wonderful, dark eyes?

Cæsar's first impulse was to grant all her demands. But there were grave difficulties in the way. He had gone to Egypt on a friendly visit and had only a few troops stationed there. Those of Ptolemy, on the other hand, were legion and well prepared to defend their sovereign. Discretion forbade rashness. This was no time to "let slip the dogs of war."

With enthusiasm, yet with a well-balanced judgment surprising in so young a woman, Cleopatra tried to touch Cæsar with her own fire. If he could not start the invasion at once, let him summon his armies as quickly as possible, and while awaiting their arrival, proclaim her reigning queen.

While she was speaking the Emperor could not take his eyes from her. He watched each rhythmic gesture, each word as it fell from her exquisite lips. "What an adorable mistress she would be!" he thought, as he breathed the perfume of her hair.

And, feeling that she had conquered him, that he was ready to do whatever she wished, Cleopatra had a thrill of delicious assurance—"In a little while I shall be queen!"

On hearing that his sister, whom he believed he had got rid of, had arrived in Alexandria, and that Cæsar had sworn to restore her to power, Ptolemy XII had one of those fits of demented rage to which this offspring of a degenerate race was subject. "The traitress!" he cried, crushing with his foot a murrhine vase of exquisite beauty. "She has tricked me. This decision that she has had the impudence to proclaim is nothing but damnable treason!" And placing Achillas in command of his troops, he massacred the Roman guard.

This was the beginning of a war which was to last two years. With all the strength of the Republic behind him it was obvious that Cæsar would win; but at the outset the insurrections and riots, with which his soldiers were not in the habit of dealing, were hard to handle.

Rather than continually encounter these street brawls, where the odds were often against him, Cleopatra's champion decided it was wiser to shut himself and his garrison up behind the walls of the Bruchium; this could, in an emergency, be used as a fort, where he could hold siege while awaiting the arrival of his army.

To be imprisoned with the man whom she was planning to captivate, so that he should have no interests other than her own—what conditions could have been more favourable to this young woman's dreams? The Bruchium, founded by Alexander, and added to by each of his successors, who, like the Pharaohs, but with a more refined taste, had a passion for building, was not merely a palace. Situated on a height, at a point where the hills which skirt the coast go down to the sea, its elaborate structures made it a city in itself; a magnificent enclosure of varied and unsurpassed splendour, where examples of massive Egyptian architecture stood side by side with graceful monuments of Greek art. The part of the palace set aside for Cleopatra had been specially arranged by Ptolemy Auletes, anxious to provide suitable surroundings for his favourite daughter. Lover of all that was rare and beautiful, this musician, no less sensitive to purity of line than to harmony of sound, had delighted in adorning it with the most perfect creations of art. At every turn were the exquisite works of Myron, Praxiteles, and Phidias; finelly carved candelabra, chairs of graceful outline, ivory coffers heavily encrusted with gold; jewelled tripods in which rare incense burned, and a wealth of carpets of marvellous and intricate design. There was no room in the gorgeous domain which did not afford a feast of form and colour to the eyes. All things seemed planned to enhance the joy of living.

But the real wonder which surpassed all else, and which could only have been found under Egyptian skies, was the stretch of gardens. Fanned by the sea breeze the air there was delicious. Terrace after terrace, connected by great marble steps, were dotted with fountains where crystal water flowed. Under the benign influence of this water, brought by aqueducts from the Nile, the vegetation was of unusual luxuriance. The green plants from more temperate climates, as well as the fig trees and palms which flourish in the tropics, grew everywhere. Flowers bloomed in profusion; rosebushes from Persia in such abundance that even the garden plots of Ecbatana seemed poor compared with those whose fragrance mounted to the windows of the Queen.

Was it strange that this son of Venus, whom the needs of war had so often compelled to endure the cold of barbarous countries, should have revelled to the point of intoxication in the delights of such an abiding-place? Everything united to bring about perfect felicity, and the grace and youth of the hostess crowned it all. From the very first he had loved her with one of those burning passions which are like the glowing sunset skies of early autumn, when summer is over and the trees are about to put on brilliant robes to surpass in colour all that has gone before.

Cleopatra gave herself unreservedly to the joys of love. Privation, exile, the dread of further persecution, all these had made her eager for happiness. Without questioning for a moment the nature of his affection, with no thought of the selfish motive behind it, she was enchanted at her triumph. Indeed, on second thoughts even, she had every reason to be satisfied. She had sought only a protector; she had found a most passionate and tender lover. Safe on board the great ship which had anchored near her coast, she had yielded to his powerful protection as to a force whose elements were not to be analyzed. If his devotion aroused no kindred sentiment in her bosom, the love of this mighty conqueror filled her with such pride, awakened such anticipations, that her heart felt no need of anything more vital. With dreams of a glorious future, she had a thrill of ecstasy at being borne along toward a destiny which, though unknown, with Cæsar for a pilot, could not fail to be one of untold splendour.

Although frequently disturbed by the noise of the catapults and the clamour of the engines, with which the besiegers were riddling the approaches to the Bruchium, the days that this pair of lovers spent there as prisoners were filled with rare delight. With no intruders to annoy them, with no other care than a continuous effort to give each other pleasure, their conversation broken only by renewed caresses, they fully realized that ideal of *solitude à deux* which so many lovers have vainly sought.

And now the armies that Cæsar had summoned began to arrive. From Cilicia and Rhodes came ships laden with provisions. This put the situation in the control of the captives and everything was in their power. Gaul sent bodies of infantry; Rome supplied the ammunition; and the cavalry, under the command of Calvinus, completed the effective force. The siege, which had lasted for six months, was now lifted and the war was carried into the open country.

Achillas's army, however, was more powerful than they had thought, and owing to its skilful tactics Cæsar was often forced into awkward positions, but with the strength and courage of Rome behind him his final success was a thing of certainty, and the beginning of the end was shown when he marshalled his men on the field of the Delta. Here the decisive battle was fought and, beaten, routed, driven into the waters of the Nile, the troops of Ptolemy were annihilated. That king met death as, on an improvised dam, he sought to leap across the flood. Cæsar, more merciful than Fate, spared the life of his opponent, Achillas, when he was brought to him in chains. He was content to receive the required reprisals, and departed in hot haste for Alexandria.

There, in the seventh story of her tower, Cleopatra was awaiting his return. When she caught the flash of his Roman eagles, amidst a cloud of dust, her heart began to throb fiercely. Unable to restrain her eagerness to see him, she ordered her litter at once. "Run quickly," she commanded her carriers, twelve Ethiopians, whose bronze legs shone as they sped swiftly over the road.

The golden hawk which soared above its roof, the gorgeous purple curtains which hung at its sides, made the royal litter visible at a great distance. At the first signal of its approach, Cæsar leaped from his horse and, with the delicate chivalry which distinguished him, greeted his beloved. He had been parted from her for several days and was longing to embrace her.

"Egypt is yours!" he exclaimed. "I have conquered it only to lay it at your feet. Accept it." And he handed her the keys of Alexandria which Achillas, in surrendering, had given up to him.

From that hour the rebels recognized the strength of the Roman power and realized the ruin that Photinus had brought upon them. From the ambitious heights of yesterday they had fallen to the desperate depths of to-day. They who had counted on reprisals were to have only amnesties; but who could have disputed the claims of the Queen that such a magnanimous conqueror had placed upon the throne? On her first appearance in public Cleopatra was acclaimed with an enthusiasm which would have been accorded her had she been the universally-designed sovereign.

Thanks to this war, which had been gained because of Cæsar's adoration, she was once more in possession of the crown of her ancestors. In order, however, to secure the good will of the people, she submitted once again to the old dynastic rule, which required children of the same parents to share the throne, and agreed to wed her younger brother, Ptolemy XIII.

All being arranged to his satisfaction, it was now time for Cæsar to leave Egypt and return to Rome where his party was clamouring for him. But Cæsar was no longer his own master. Given over to that passion which, to the end of his life, was to be the mainspring of all his actions, to come before duty, ambition, self-interest, and lead to his final downfall, he delayed his departure. Deaf to the warning that each new messenger brought, he heeded only the voice of the dear enchantress who, in addition to all the other spells with which she had held him, now suggested the delight of a voyage together.

In those days, as in our own, sailing along the borders of the Nile, with the monuments of the Pharaohs on either side, was a fascinating experience. Aristocrats of wealth, princes from the Orient, artists from Asia Minor and Greece—after exploring the treasures of Alexandria—alike found rare pleasure in sailing in the luxurious Egyptian barges under the smiling skies. These voyages meant weeks of restful leisure and enjoyment.

The barge of Cleopatra was a floating palace. The charming apartments of the Bruchium were reproduced in miniature. The various vessels which accompanied it accommodated a large staff, not of servants alone, but bands of dancers, poets, musicians, who were engaged to while away the time and make life an enchanting dream.

Winter was at hand; that season of snow and frost which, in less fortunate lands, plunges people in gloom; when all the fields are in mourning and the shivering trees wave their naked branches in distress. But there was no depression along the sunny route chosen by our travellers. Propelled by the steady rowing of fifty Nubians pulling on oars of ebony, they glided along, intoxicated with freedom, happiness, space, as toward a Promised Land, and at each stopping-place the golden sun seemed to shine with a richer glow.

All at once, after the leagues of emerald foliage of the first few days, the vegetation grew scanty, the barge slipped along between barren shores, and the country, as far as the distant horizon, was a vast stretch of sand covered with arid hillocks, like volutes of silver, which melted away in the mist. Here and there groups of aloes waved their sharp, blade-like branches, or clusters of date trees shook their feathery plumes, like giant torches about to burst into flame.

As the barge approached Memphis more buildings were seen: temples with broad columns, shining palaces of glittering whiteness, giant gateways like mighty mountains, all mirrored in the waters of the sacred river.

The barge dropped anchor opposite the Pyramids. Cæsar was filled with wondering admiration at the mighty skill which had reared these colossal tombs. He who, as a disciple of Plato, attached so little importance to the needs of the body, and who believed that immortality was attained only by the beauty which came from the soul, asked himself what thoughts had stirred the mind of a Cheops or a Chephren concerning the mystery of Death?

Had they regarded it as the true life, and the earthly one merely as a passage leading to it? Had they raised these temples in honour of Death, or, indignant at its devastations, was it in defiance of it that they had erected these formidable triangles?

Among the countless mysterious monuments on the plains about Memphis, the great Sphinx of Gizeh has always aroused the keenest wonder and curiosity. Cleopatra had caught a glimpse of it in the distance on her adventurous flight and now she was overjoyed at letting Cæsar compare her delicate grace with its tremendous proportions. The sun was setting behind the Libyan hills when they drew near the Sphinx. Lying on her bed of sand, the monster seemed about to emerge from a vast beach beside a congealed ocean. Although looking toward the East, her enigmatic smile already hidden in the shadow, her tawny back was touched by the last rays of the setting sun, which made her like a living creature.

Recalling the question that Œdipus, anxious concerning his future, had put to that other Sphinx long ago, the Dictator, whose destiny also was uncertain, was tempted to interrogate this one. Would she reply? Mystery of mysteries! Quivering at the touch of the warm young body at his side, looking at the reddish moon, breathing in the strange soul of the night, even had some wise counsel been whispered in his ear he was hardly in a state to heed it. The voice of love was too overpowering, he was deaf to all else.

On the thirtieth day of their voyage the lovers reached Philæ, that pearl in its double setting of blue sky and blue water, both so pure, so transparent, that it was difficult to tell which was the reflection of the other, which has inspired the poets of every age. Those who once entered there went no further to seek an earthly paradise. To tarry, pitch their tent, and forget in the worship of its beauty all that had fretted and distracted them elsewhere, was the ardent desire of every artist who landed there. Only a few, however, were allowed to carry it out.

From remote ages the island had been in possession of the priests of Isis, who did not tolerate the intrusion of profane outsiders. Guardians of a temple which the religious fervour of its worshippers had made the richest in all Egypt, these priests of the holy goddess allowed no interference with their rights; no one else was permitted to share the revenue, which was the largest in the land.

In many of the sanctuaries, however, the religious rites were in no way disturbed by the addition of worldly goods; consequently the arrival of the royal visitors was regarded as a godsend. Barges, filled with musicians, were sent down the river to welcome them, and along the banks a procession of priests greeted them with sacred songs. They were forced to attend the services in the temple, listen to orations, and receive committees bearing gifts. To celebrate their coming, goats were sacrificed and the blood of doves ran red.

The official reception over, Cleopatra requested that she and Cæsar be left alone, quite undisturbed by any formalities, since that was their chief desire. During the heat of the day they remained indoors, where the spray from numerous fountains made the air comparatively cool. They amused themselves watching the blue, white, and pink lotus buds open their delicate petals, both lost in a delicious languor in which cares, plans, ambitions, were all forgotten.

The young Queen, however, never for a moment forgot the secret object of this voyage, which was to bind her great protector to her by indelible memories and make Egypt's interests his own. In the evenings they loitered along the garden paths, breathing the honey-scented fragrance of the tropical violets, or lingered in the shadowy groves whose branches sent showers of gold dust on their heads. Here, in response to her lover's tender speeches, she would reply, in a tone of almost childish terror: "Oh! yes, of course my country is the most beautiful in all the world, but it is so difficult to govern it." And Cæsar, moved by the frailty of the slender arm about his neck, would with deep earnestness pledge her the perpetual and all-powerful support of his own country.

Although this absence from public life could not be prolonged indefinitely, these lovers wished at least to commemorate the happy memory of these days together. A plan for a temple was drawn up, and, before leaving the island, in a space surrounded by oleander trees, where birds of brilliant plumage flitted in and out, they laid the corner-stone. Two thousand years have gone by, and the pilgrims who in each succeeding age have visited the paradise of Philæ have gazed in admiration on the exquisite marble colonnade of pure Corinthian design which stands there in delicate beauty. The name of no goddess is carved upon its stone, but each pilgrim knows to whom it is dedicated.

At Alexandria a delegation awaited Cæsar. When Rome heard that the conqueror of the Pharaohs, the hero on whom his country's hopes relied, was dallying with a new Circe, there was general consternation. Did he think that he could defy Fate? What his good fortune and his genius had built, his neglect could destroy. What would happen if the allies of Pompey, knowing that Cæsar was distracted by a love affair, should mobilize new troops? The more daring among these were already on the alert and threats were in the air.

However sweet a pillow a woman's breast may be, a man of Cæsar's stamp is roused by the call of his friends: "Your honour is at stake." At the sound of the voice of those who had come to seek him, the lover started from his sleep. He knew that all his mighty deeds would count for nothing if he did not respond to the appeal of the hour. He must go at once. He *would* go, but he must have time to break the tidings to the woman who had put her trust in him. With all possible tenderness he told Cleopatra of the coming separation.

"Ah!" she cried, "you wish to unwind my arms from about your neck?" and with a passionate gesture she held him closer, and Cæsar, strong against the world, was weak against his loved one. He hesitated; then, happily remembering the maxim which had guided him through life: "The first, always, and everywhere," his courage came again. He was not an ordinary voluptuary whose instinct was his master. His noble temperament demanded action and the strain of public life was essential to him. "Shall I," he muttered, "who have looked on mankind as a vile herd, become by cowardly inertia like unto those I scorn?"

Cleopatra was overcome with grief at the thought of losing him. How would she fare with Cæsar far away? Who would protect and defend her? Who would help her to govern her capricious and deceitful people? She was about to become a mother and, relying on this new tie which would bind her lover to her, she made him promise not to leave her before the birth of her child.

And Cæsar was much interested in the expected birth; what he had said to her regarding the coming child had given Cleopatra ground for the most exalted hopes. It had been a source of keen regret to him that none of his three wives had given him an heir. He had been particularly anxious since the death of his daughter Julia, and the consequent loss of her fortune. To whom should he leave his boundless wealth, that vast estate that he owned in Umbria? Who would carry on the divine race of the Cæsars?

To be sure, his sister Atia had a son, Octavius, but this nephew was in delicate health, of a weak, undecided character, which did not promise a brilliant future. Who could tell whether the coming bastard would not be a more worthy heir to the glorious fortunes of the Emperor?

The baby was born on the very eve of the day that the friends of Cæsar, worn out with waiting, had made him agree to set sail. It was a boy! By wonderful chance the scarcely-formed features of the tiny creature showed an undeniable resemblance to those of his father. The hearts of those who are beginning to grow old are naturally easily moved, and the Emperor's joy in his new-born son was very evident. He decided to call him Cæsarion and promised to adopt him. In a touching farewell scene, filled with reproaches and protestations, Cleopatra expressed the cherished desire of her heart: "Make me your wife, O Cæsar!" Her dainty head, adorned with her restored crown, was filled with new aspirations. She was no longer content with ruling the country of her ancestors. It had lost prestige and was now scarcely more than a commercial power. Her secret dream was to link her destiny with that of the master of the Roman Empire.

At first Cæsar was alarmed at this suggestion. In the royal palace on the Aventine, Calpurnia, his lawful wife, awaited his return. Cleopatra herself was married, bound by the tradition of her line. But what were such obstacles to the youthful heroine who had measured the world and found it none too large for her ambitions? She laid stress on what it would mean to them both, this contract which, uniting the vast riches of the one with the warlike genius of the other, would make all things possible for them.

The prospect was magnificent and Cæsar was tempted. He understood how well it fitted in with his own passion for his royal mistress. But would Rome allow him to carry it out? One of the strictest laws of the Roman Senate forbade the marriage of Patricians with foreigners. "But are you not above the law?" said the loved voice of the temptress. What man could resist being placed in the ranks of the gods?

It was the moment of farewell. Overcome, Cæsar took Cleopatra in a final embrace. There was no formal engagement but, with the departure of her lover, she felt the solemnity of a betrothal.

Left alone, her imagination ran riot; and she was lost in fantastic dreams. She had visions of a Rome humiliated, submissive to the will of Alexandria. Vassals crouched at her feet, coming to lay down their arms and present the keys of their different capitals. Multitudes passed before her, and she fancied she heard her name coupled with that of Cæsar, amidst general acclamation. Happy in such dreams, her solitude was transformed, it was no longer a desolate, arid plain; the stage changed and the coveted goal seemed more real than the dull present.

Once free from the sorcery which the dark, velvet eyes of the Egyptian had thrown over him, Cæsar was himself again; shrewd, clear-minded, quick at wise decisions. His eagle eye took in things at a glance. The conditions were far from being what they had been at Pharsalus. No longer dreading him, the army of Pompey had had time to reorganize. It was threatening him on every side. The danger seemed more imminent in the Orient; so, before returning to Italy, the Emperor set sail for Asia Minor and began by destroying the enemy's fleet which was blocking the entrance to the Cydnus; then, with an army of tried veterans, from whom he could demand miracles, he attacked Caius Cassius at Ephesus, Pharnaces at Zela, returned to Africa and there won the battle of Thapsus. After having gained vast sums from the terrified rulers, in exchange for certain territories which he granted the enemy, he reëntered Rome, laden with spoils, to calm the malcontents.

Triumph awaited Cæsar, such a triumph as the Via Sacra had never seen before. Beholding him crowned with laurels, followed by a procession of captive kings, and greater than them all, by the illustrious Vercingetorix, who represented the opposing armies of Gaul, the Roman people forgot their grievances. Around his chariot, on which was inscribed in letters of gold the famous phrase, *Veni, vidi, vici,* the crowd flocked with the enthusiasm of children welcoming a long-lost father. The Aristocracy was more reserved; it was to the People that the Dictator looked for support; it was to improve their conditions that his first reforms were brought about. But he understood this unstable mass, and the sudden changes that their whims effected, too thoroughly to confine his reforms to serious benefits alone. To amuse the populace has always been the surest means of holding it. Consequently Cæsar ordered festivals and banquets. In every quarter of the city wheat was distributed, and oil and wine were provided in abundance. There was acting of plays; the circuses were filled with crowds, eager to watch the slaughter of gladiators and look on as the blood flowed from the wounded beasts. The orgy lasted forty days and during all that time there was but one opinion. Cæsar was the *Illustrious,* the *Invincible,* the *beloved Father of his Country.* Every title and every honour was bestowed upon him. He was Consul, Dictator for Ten Years. He received the insignia of the great Pontiff. His chair of state was placed above all the other chairs, and on the statue erected to him in the temple of Jupiter the word "God" was chiselled.

At Alexandria, however, things were not going so smoothly. In spite of the troops which Cæsar had left, under the command of Calvinus, to maintain order, seditious outbreaks occurred. More or less openly the Queen was accused of having decoyed the alien, of having become the mistress of a Roman, and of compromising the honour of the kingdom by declaring him to be the father of her child. Did she mean to put as future king over the Egyptians one who was not of their own race? Such accusations would have had no weight with any one strong enough to ignore them. But Cleopatra was not yet the dauntless ruler who later on was to defy public opinion and lead her own armies to battle. At twenty years of age she was sensitive; she shuddered at these whispers of revolution. The protector who had restored her throne and made her respected thereon was no longer at her side; she was uneasy. Could she always withstand these snares, these threats, these uprisings? Until now Cæsar's influence, even in his absence, had been strong enough to shield her. But if these insurrectionists should think her deserted, dependent only on her own resources, of what attempt would they not be capable? Besides, foul rumours were abroad. It was said that during the expedition in Africa the Emperor had amused himself with the

Queen Eunonia. Was it possible? So soon after leaving her bosom where he had sworn to be faithful to her forever? Ah, how powerless is woman when her lover is no longer within reach of her encircling arms!

But the distance between them was not impassable. If it were true, as his letters declared, that Cæsar loved her still and was desolate at being so far away from her, why should she not go to him? The desire to strengthen, lest it become too lax, the bond which united them was mixed with a certain curiosity in regard to Rome itself. Rome, her hereditary foe; that rival against whom perpetual vigilance was needed. Seen at close quarters a rival is less deadly, for one can find ways of opposing her. Cleopatra decided to suggest the visit to Cæsar.

After a year's absence from her, his letters declared that he cared for her as deeply as ever. If he had been attracted by the Queen of Numidia, it had been but a passing fancy, or rather the need, through some diversion, to escape the memories which were taking too much of his time. Burdened with grave responsibilities, did he have any right to be so absorbed in his love affairs? Indeed he was always going back, sometimes with a degree of intensity over which he had no control, to the affecting scenes at the Bruchium, or recalling the hours when he had been lulled to slumber by the soothing waters of the Nile.

Cæsar did not agree immediately, however, to the proposed visit. To have the Queen of Egypt come to Rome was a serious undertaking. He would not wish to run the risk until everything had been made smooth for the trip. The gravest difficulty lay in the natural antipathy of the Romans to everyone who wore a crown. It might almost be said that this sentiment was so deeply rooted that the mere approach of royalty seemed to endanger the monarchy. Now Cleopatra was an especial object of distrust. She was known to be ambitious, and no one had forgotten the spell she had cast over Cæsar. The discontent that had been felt momentarily toward him was now directed against her. In order to clear the one they accused the other, and the blame fell upon her. A woman must have had strange powers to have kept the Emperor away from his own country for such a long time; to have detained him at such a great distance from those who had the strongest claims upon him!

How far was it wise to bring his mistress amongst such adverse opinions? Cæsar put the question to himself. He did not dare to expose her to a hostile reception; still less could he afford to disregard the enemies who were ready to resent his shortest absence in order to go to her.

And so the days went by and Cleopatra was filled with grief and indignation.

It was from her that the final decision came which solved the vexed question. Pretending that the conditions of her treaty with Rome had never been settled, she offered to come in person to discuss several disputable clauses. In order to obtain the title of *socius republicæ* (ally of the Republic) it was not in the least necessary for the Queen to go herself; the different ambassadors could have attended to the matter; but the Roman Senate, flattered by her preferring to deal directly with it, extended her an invitation. The trick had succeeded. There was nothing more to do but to start on the journey.

The June sun was shining brilliantly. With her Forum alive, her windows crowded, the multitudes ranged along the principal thoroughfares, Rome seemed to be holding a festival. Defiance, however, rather than sympathy, was the spirit of the crowd. Many strange stories were afloat concerning the coming visitor. To some, she was a courtesan, glittering with pearls and gold; to others, she was a sorceress, whose evil influence drove to distraction all those who came near her. For the majority, Cleopatra was simply the alien, the woman from the East, that is to say, the thing that the Roman people despised more than anything on earth. The procession was composed of black slaves wearing gold ear-rings; of eunuchs clothed in long robes, like those worn by women; of ministers with their heavy wigs; of half-naked soldiers (whose heads, adorned with antennæ, resembled huge insects). When it began to file past, there were shouts of laughter. Derision greeted the appearance of the astronomers, whose pointed caps seemed reaching toward the sky, and the priests muffled in panther skins. The jeering grew louder at the sight of the standards on which sacred images were painted. What, those jackals, those hawks, those cows! They were meant for gods? And the Latin commonsense rebelled against a religion debased by such emblems.

But in the midst of the flashing splendour of spears and shields, the royal litter was seen. Silence reigned and all eyes were fixed on Cleopatra with her baby in her arms. This child, a cause of embarrassment to her at Alexandria, it was on his winning smile, on his astonishing likeness to Cæsar, that she had relied to gain a warm welcome from the Romans. And she was not mistaken. At this time Cæsar was the idol of Rome. Everything he did was approved, and if there were covert sneers and occasionally harsh criticisms, no one would have dared openly to attack his invited guests.

However beautiful she might be, the Queen of Egypt could not hope to please a people so infatuated with themselves as were the Romans, who looked on their own race as superior to all others. With her golden complexion, her eyes so painted with antimony that they seemed to touch her temples, her vivid red lips, her curious headdress, from which a snake of gold peered forth; her transparent tunic, which left her bosom bare, Cleopatra shocked and scandalized the Roman people. But, as Cæsar's orders made graciousness obligatory, they pretended to be absorbed in the tiny Cæsarion, whose fair skin and quick, intelligent expression indicated his divine ancestry.

Moreover, in order that there should be no mistake in regard to the respect due Cleopatra and her son, Cæsar had installed them in the palace which he had just had built on the left side of the Tiber, overlooking the magnificent gardens along the edge of the hill of Janiculum; those gardens which were left to the populace in his will, which generous gift the day after his death brought the people to their knees, in tears, to look upon his blood-stained toga.

On finding herself, at last, the honoured guest of

Rome, Cleopatra felt that keen pleasure of achievement which follows a hard struggle for success. In spite of all obstacles she had, to her entire satisfaction, accomplished the first part of her undertaking.

But the essential thing, the real triumph, was yet to be carried out. She must bind her lover by that long-desired marriage which would make her twice a Queen. For a woman of her talent, accustomed to using her varied powers of fascination to gain her ends, the present situation was ideal. Rome, from the very moment that she had entered its gates, had ceased to be the austere stronghold, where each and every citizen, faithful to his Lares and Penates, was steadfast in revering ancient traditions. These traditions, which had made the strength and greatness of the Republic as well as its formidable power, were already losing their hold. The old religion was passing; although still acknowledged by the State, unbelievers were many, especially among the Aristocracy. If the people had still a certain fear of the gods, this did not prevent them from breaking the laws of their deities, or from desecrating their temples in moments of passion. The story of the cynical soldier who boasted of having stolen the statue of Diana and of having made a fortune by this godless act was a common tale. The inviolability of the marriage law was a thing of the past. On every hand, Senators, Consuls, high dignitaries, put away their wives on the slightest pretext. Cicero himself, the best, the gentlest of men, said to Terentia, his wife for thirty years, the cruel words of divorcement: "Go hence and take with you whatever belongs to you," in order to put a younger, more beautiful woman in her place.

This disregard of the morals and manners of the old régime was a general canker, pervading all classes of Roman society. Shocking scandals marked the closing days of the circus, when it was a common occurrence for the nobles to descend into the arena and measure arms with the gladiators. The immense fortunes, accumulated during the war, had wiped out the simple habits of former days. Gold was the god that reigned supreme. Originally used for the decoration of the temples only, it was now displayed in private houses, where furniture, ceilings, walls, everything, was gilded. As a protest against the wanton luxury of his contemporaries Cato made a practice of walking about bare-footed, in a torn toga; but no one followed his example! He was merely ridiculed, while the procession of gorgeous chariots rolled on. No longer restrained by the Oppian law, the women's extravagance in dress knew no limit. Encircling their arms, twisted in their hair, clasping their ankles, golden ornaments of Etruscan workmanship glittered over them from head to foot; about their necks fell jewelled chains, which had been brought, at fabulous cost, from the rich caverns of India.

The banquets that were served at the tables of the wealthy Patricians rivalled those of Lucullus. The dishes of silver, the richly carved goblets, the heavy purple draperies of the couches, equalled in magnificence those of oriental sovereigns. Dignity, along with the once-revered virtues of economy, sobriety, endurance, all that Rome had stood for in the old days, was becoming a mere legend of the past.

But if the old society was changing, giving place to a new era which lacked the dignity of its predecessor, it is certain that the actual joy of living was materially increased. The culture of letters, the pursuit of art, had never been so widely spread. The philosophy, the sculpture, the language even, of Greece—which cultivated people prided themselves on speaking perfectly—had been born anew in the Rome of that day. There was no aristocratic youth who did not as a matter of course finish his education at Rhodes, Apollonia, or, best of all, at Athens. The theories that they learned there were universally accepted. A knowledge of literature was general in the higher ranks of society, where formerly it had been the exclusive privilege of the so-called intellectuals. It became the fashion to be learned. Many patrician homes aspired to the honour of entertaining a savant or a philosopher. It was considered a particular distinction to have the youthful Virgil, recently arrived from Mantua, as a guest, and to hear him recite his gracious pastorals at evening entertainments; or to listen to the verses of that poem, forged on the ringing anvil which was to resound down the ages, sung by Horace, then a youth of twenty years. In fact, everywhere, from whatever source it sprang, talent was held in high esteem.

Cleopatra understood at once the tremendous part that her personal charm could play in a society eager for everything that was new, original, and interesting. Probably she alone, among all the women there, was in a position to attract to her apartments learned men from all countries, and to furnish them with liberal, amusing recreation. Endowed with the rare and fascinating advantage of an understanding and spirit unequalled either by the Roman matrons, absorbed in their household affairs, or by the famous courtesans, whose conversation was often both frivolous and ribald, she had every reason to be confident of success.

In the sumptuous hall, which her artistic taste had adorned with luxurious divans, rich rugs, splendid draperies, she entertained the friends of Cæsar, who, happy in having his latest *inamorata* restored to him, came every evening to forget at her side the political cares of the day. He enjoyed meeting his friends there informally, though all the while looking forward to the hour when he would clasp her lissome, perfumed body, and feel her heart beat against his own.

Trebonius, Lepidus, Sulpicius Rufus, Curion, and other Senators of congenial tastes were always to be found there. They discussed the leading questions of the hour; the means for carrying out promises made to the troops; the abolition of debts, reduction of rents. In all these debates they were surprised to hear this young woman, who apparently was there only to illuminate the room with her shining eyes, or to charm the hearers by the tinkling of her bracelets, give grave advice on these important matters and show in all things a wise judgment. Their astonishment grew greater on overhearing her conversation with the historian Sallust, whose writing and psychology she had studied and appreciated.

Her comments were trenchant and convincing. The orator Asinius Pollion delighted in bringing his serious speeches to her for criticism, as well as those little ironical poems in which, speaking through the mouth of a shepherd, he ridiculed the absurdities of his fellow-citizens. Her arguments and criticism were marvels of intelligent thought. Her discussions with the archæologist, Atticus, in whose discoveries she was much interested, when he unrolled the delicately illuminated Persian scrolls, pointed out a bit of ivory polished by the patient skill of a Chinese workman, or showed her a fragment of bas-relief from the temple of Ephesus, all these indicated an unusual mind, alive to wide-reaching interests. Who would not have been moved at seeing this young girl poring over that chart of the heavens, on which a congress of savants was engaged in their alteration of the calendar; or watching her follow the evolution of the Great Bear, of Cassiopeia, of Orion, around the North Star? Truly in all things she was an exceptional creature, one of those chosen by the deities to represent them on earth.

It was at this time that Mark Antony, young, handsome, renowned, was presented to her. He had just arrived from Spain, covered with laurels won at Munda and laden with spoils. The fame of incomparable valour had given him a crown of glory. With his athletic body, the Bacchus-like smile which lighted up his face, his generous extravagance, he made a heroic figure, recalling the mythical Hercules, from whom he claimed descent. Although for the moment enamoured of the courtesan

Cytheris, the young soldier was deeply impressed by the bewildering beauty of Cleopatra and it was only his sincere devotion to Cæsar which prevented him from expressing his admiration openly. He could not forget any single detail of their first meeting: the queenly grace with which the enchantress stretched out her tiny hand for him to kiss, the dress she wore that first evening, or the sudden anguish that thrilled him at the sound of her voice.

However enthusiastic was the adoration of this new Aspasia within that sanctuary of art and literature which her villa had become, a pack of wolves was snarling just outside. It was made up of virtuous, or pretendedly virtuous, men, indignant at the generally accepted and avowed liaison of the Dictator with this foreign woman. All the women of position in Rome were with them. The majority of them had endured humiliation at the hands of their husbands, and these embittered wives were leagued together in jealous persecution of this oriental sorceress of loose morals, whose dwelling was thronged with the men who had deserted their own firesides to seek her.

But Cleopatra's worst enemies were her political foes. Bound by ancient traditions, the Conservatives were uneasy at these new proceedings, which tended more and more to encroach on old customs. For some time it had been well known that Cæsar's ambition and personal desire were goading him to seek sovereign power; but, however evident had been the pomp with which he loved to surround himself, it was on his royal mistress that the chief blame fell. Was he giving up pious ways, did he disregard the laws, was he careless of all that Rome held most sacred? It was the accursed Egyptian who was responsible for all.

Whether or not it was the fault of the fair foreigner, it was evident that each day Cæsar strayed further and further from republican forms. Since the wars were over, there was no excuse for his prolonging his dictatorship. He was now absolute arbitrator and controlled all the affairs of the State. He chose the officers and divided the confiscated territories as he pleased. Where would his power stop? The title of King itself could not increase this power, but the feeling prevailed that he coveted that title and would seize the first opportunity to assume it. So far from consulting his colleagues as to ways and means, according to the established usage among Senators, Consuls, and Pontiffs, he seemed to delight in defying them, and showing the public that he looked on their opinions as antiquated, if not obsolete. With an insolence reeking of the *grand seigneur,* a lord who had flung off the traditions of his caste, he deliberately ridiculed the ethics of Cato, and was skeptical of everything, including the gods themselves. Had he not declared in the open Senate, among other imprudent sayings which had been noised abroad and exaggerated, that "The Republic from now on is a word without meaning?"

Cicero was leader of the party most genuinely alarmed by this state of things. The great orator was, after Cæsar, the first citizen of Rome. At all events he was the most honest and among those most respected. His liberal views had formerly associated him with Pompey's party and, since the latter's defeat, he had lived in retirement in his villa at Tusculum, given over to meditation. It had been a keen regret to Cæsar to lose the friendship of this warm-hearted man whose distinguished ability was so widely known and who would have been an invaluable adviser. The withdrawal of so important a figure had also been a blow to Cleopatra's pride. To entice him to her home, to number him among her courtiers, to make him an ally against the day when it might be necessary to break the law to gain her ends; with all her boundless ambition, this idea became a veritable obsession.

She unbosomed herself to Atticus, who was an intimate friend of Cicero. Attached as he was to the Queen whose hospitality had afforded him so many agreeable hours, he promised to use his influence with Cicero. No one was better fitted for the duties of ambassador. To bring together, to reconcile, to persuade, were intrinsic qualities of his serene nature. He was undoubtedly helped in his mission by the insufferable *ennui* which was consuming Cicero. For a man who had known the intoxication of power, who had been applauded in tones to shake the columns of the temples, there was no worse punishment than to be forced into seclusion. In order to hear again the praises of the crowd which was eager for him, to accept the homage which awaited him, and, above all, to enjoy the splendour of Cleopatra's library, where he would be free to read to his heart's content, the man of letters yielded to temptation and appeared at her portals, wrapped in the toga which no one knew so well as he how to drape about the shoulders. Cæsar was there to welcome him.

Cleopatra, radiant as always when one of her caprices had triumphed, received her distinguished guest with every honour. To please his connoisseur's taste, that first evening she drew his attention to the interesting things in her luxurious dwelling. One table was covered with antique parchments, embellished with curious drawings, depicting the history of the Pharaohs. The orator with his delicate hands would unroll these time-yellowed pages, and, while he was admiring the singular figures of the Egyptian hieroglyphics, the Queen would translate the meaning of the script in her cultivated, sweet-toned voice. Seeing his keen interest she thought him already won, but to make sure she promised that the precious writings should be sent to him at Tusculum the very next day.

A man of Cicero's character, however, was not so easily beguiled. If, after the various pledges made to the Conservative party, he had for the moment believed that Cæsar would return to his old liberal views, the recent outbreaks, the arbitrary proceedings, left him no shadow of illusion. Without a doubt the fall of the Republic was close at hand, and nowhere did the patriotic old man find an atmosphere more repugnant to his cherished ideals than in the court of the Transtevera. Gradually he stopped attending the sessions there. He felt freer to express his opinions outside its doors, and, alluding probably to the mixed crowd, enthusiastic but vulgar, which Cæsar's popularity had attracted, he replied to Atticus's query as to the cause of his absence: "I cannot be content in a place so devoid of civility."

This criticism, as well as other comments on his attitude, made no impression on Cæsar. He saw no need of concessions, especially if they were demanded by minds less daring than his own. The one thing necessary to establish his authority was the carrying out of some yet more brilliant project. To attain the height of his dream the old weapons were out of date. New expeditions, new wars even, must be planned; something that would surpass in splendour all his other achievements.

The country that attracted his adventurous spirit, tempted him with the most entrancing visions, was Persia; that Persia which had been the scene of the world-famous exploits of Alexander. Its boundless territory, its high plateaus, which pastured peaceful herds; its valleys, watered by the abundant streams of the Tigris and the Euphrates; its hanging gardens, its palaces of porphyry, its temples with their crowned columns; its incomparable rugs, its roses, its porcelains—all the fascinating possibilities of this kingdom called him, and the appeal was irresistible.

How different it was from poor, bare, barbarous Gaul! If he could perch his eagles in Persia, he would gain not only glory, a glory equal to that of the victorious Macedonian, but the inexhaustible riches of the country.

Cleopatra was even more enthusiastic than Cæsar in the pursuit of this wonderful vision. With no illusions as to the hatred which surrounded her, she fully realized that the only way to make the stern

Roman aristocracy accept her presence was through the mighty power of Cæsar. To augment this power, to extend it from the borders of the Orient to her own country, to build a pedestal so high that from it she could see the whole world, was the ambition of the young Queen. So, although it was hard to leave the palace where she had so calmly and persistently played her part as a great lady of Rome, harder still to go back to Egypt and rejoin the clown whom she had accepted for her husband, she began to make ready for the journey.

It was generally known that when the Dictator came back from the campaign in Persia he would celebrate their wedding and adopt the son that she had given him. Certain malcontents declared that to the supreme power, which now equalled that of any king, Cæsar would then add the royal sceptre, and that he was planning to found a far-reaching empire, whose capital would be Alexandria. These rumours disturbed the people; they wounded them in their tenderest spot, their desire for the supremacy of their beloved Rome. To threaten it with division, with possible downfall, aroused the fiercest passions of the multitude.

As usual, the responsibility for these evil schemes fell on Cleopatra. The hatred of her was redoubled. Her enemies invented fantastic tales and circulated the dreadful accusation that she sealed her oaths with the avowal: "As surely as that one day I shall rule Rome." When they heard this the wrath of the multitude overflowed. When her litter appeared in the street, there was a riot. On every hand there were threats of compelling this

Egyptian interloper to leave the country, of forcing her to return to her own land of crocodiles!

These disrespectful speeches naturally came to Cæsar's ears. They angered him more than the criticisms of his own conduct. To dare to desecrate the sacred one whom he had chosen! To approach her with lack of reverence! It was not to be tolerated! Alluding to a special group which had offended him, he exclaimed: "You shall see the penalty that I will inflict on those greasy, curly-pated slanderers!"

He immediately summoned Timomachus, who for the past month had been working on a statue of the Queen, made of ivory overlaid with gold.

"How long will it take to finish that piece of sculpture?" he demanded.

The sculptor reflected, estimated the time needed for the required incrustations of gold, which were not even begun, and answered, awkwardly,

"Twenty years, at least."

"I will give you three days," declared the Dictator. "In three days I desire that statue to be placed on its pillar in the temple of Venus-Genitrix."

The autocratic temper of Cæsar, which frequently brought on violent crises owing to his delicate, overwrought nerves, was too well known for any one to dare to oppose his wishes. The dedication of the statue took place with great ceremony on the day specified, and with rage in their hearts, priests, noblemen, officers of all ranks were compelled to bow before this new goddess who had invaded their temple.

A little later, in order to see how far he could

brave public opinion, Cæsar devised a new experiment. It was at the festival of Lupercalia, a carnival lasting several days, during which the young Patricians ran half naked through the streets, striking in jest the passers-by with leather thongs, under pretext of bringing them good luck. In his position of grand Pontiff, Cæsar presided at the festival. Seated in the Tribune, in a chair of gold and ivory, he had Cleopatra by his side. After the earth had been sprinkled with the blood of goats and dogs, according to the customary rites, he was about to withdraw, when Mark Antony, pushing his way through the crowd, boldly offered him a diadem. At this movement a murmur arose, like the sound of the sea before a coming storm. Cæsar felt that it was not the moment for such a display and he turned away. But, urged on by the Queen, who perhaps was the original instigator of the comedy, Mark Antony insisted on proffering the glittering crown. The angry murmur increased; it sounded now as though the wind were rushing through the waves. Decidedly this was not an auspicious hour. With a sterner gesture than before, a gesture which left no room for doubt, Cæsar threw back his head and thrust aside the tempting jewel. All the world was witness, he had refused to be crowned as King!

Many of the spectators, deceived by the scene which had just taken place, applauded furiously. Others, keener-sighted, detected signs of a plot, and said to each other: "Oh, no doubt he refuses to-day, but only to accept more graciously when he shall come back, bearing the standards of victory!" And in dark corners conspirators began to gather.

Spring was drawing near. It was about the middle of the month consecrated to the god of War. Blown by strong winds the tiny clouds scudded across the faint blue sky. The quivering trees began to swell and the crests of the seven hills around Rome were touched with vivid green. At their base lay the city, shrouded in the dim evening light. The clamour of the streets slowly died out and silence reigned. It was the hour when, the day's work done, each was going to his own home. This was the time when Cæsar, absorbed all day by his preparations for war, was hastening toward the dwelling of his beloved and beautiful mistress.

Seated near the window, from which she could see him coming, Cleopatra was lost in dreams. A few more days and they must part. While Cæsar was seeking fresh conquests through the Caspian gates she would be once more on the borders of the Nile. The coming separation made her anxious, suggested painful isolation and unknown difficulties. She was resigned, however, for she knew it was inevitable. Was not glory as necessary to rulers as bread to the common people? Master of Persia, Cæsar would be lord of all. No human power could then prevent them from carrying out their plans. He would place her on the thrones of Nineveh and Babylon, and proclaim her as his lawful wife. Together they would build their capital and this same Rome, which she had heard roaring like an infuriated she-wolf whenever she passed, would be compelled to receive her with acclamation.

It was on these mighty visions, on this dream of

Semiramis, that the dreadful thunderbolt of the Ides of March was about to fall.

Morning had just come. Cæsar had left her scarcely an hour before, and in leaving had crushed her to his heart as though he would never let her go. By one of those mysterious forebodings which sometimes come in moments of decisive action and which should never be ignored, she had tried to detain him. "Why are you going so early? You said you were tired. Stay here and rest." But, no, he was expected. For fear lest he be late Brutus had sent Cassius to meet him, and, with no flinching of his traitor face, the latter had told him he must make haste, that there were matters of grave importance awaiting him in the Senate.

And it was there that the blow fell. A sudden noise was heard. "Hark, what was that?" The passers-by halted to ask what had happened. Suddenly the portico was filled with blanched faces. There was a terrifying cry: "Cæsar is assassinated!" Wailing was heard on every side, but it was drowned by the yells of the murderers, who, swords in hand, surged around, shrieking: "We have avenged the honour of the Republic!"

Horrified, not knowing what to believe, the people scattered, like a river that had burst its dam, and spread all over the city. In a moment the frightful news reached all quarters of Rome. Disorder and consternation reigned. The shops were quickly closed; each man hid his terror behind the shutters of his house. All knew that an overwhelming disaster had fallen on Rome and that others, many others, were treading closely on its heels.

To Cleopatra it meant the end of all her hopes. A great black gulf seemed to open at her feet, swallowing in its hungry depths her whole future. The world was a desert.

Gangs of armed men ran along the shores of the Tiber, waving batons surmounted by skull-caps, the Roman symbol of liberty. They paused under the windows of the royal palace. Fierce cries rang out on the air of that fair spring morning.

"Down with the Egyptian woman! Put her to death! Put her to death!" They were the same voices that spring up the world over, in every age, at the sign of revolution. Some attendants gathered around the Queen, eager to defend her; but they were too distracted to afford any certainty of protection.

Apollodorus, alone, whose stern commonsense never deserted him in the most critical moments, spoke quickly, and with authority:

"Your Majesty must quit this bloody town without delay!"

But it was not in Cleopatra's nature to yield to threats, and she rebelled. Her instinct was to resist this mob. Perhaps all was not yet lost. Cæsar would surely have avengers. A party had already formed, with Antony at its head. He had loved the dead Cæsar, and would be likely to respect his wishes, to recognize the young Cæsarion as his lawful son, the proper heir to. . . .

This was only an illusion; an illusion which, if persisted in, would be disastrous. In the prevailing tumults neither the child nor his mother would be safe. The cries grew louder. There was nothing to do but heed the counsel of Apollodorus. With his ingenuity and affection he had already made all necessary preparations for flight.

Through the same gardens, along dangerous paths, surrounded by spies, the scene of four years ago—when she had come, a persecuted girl, to Cæsar for protection—was repeated, and Cleopatra, heavily veiled, slipped out of the hostile city of Rome.

As she journeyed on she felt sometimes almost overwhelmed by the racking anguish of her heart. It seemed as though the earth were giving way under her feet. Horror! Desolation! To be alone, when so short a while before she had had the Master of the World for her companion! The thought made her dizzy. But at her breast was the tiny head bearing the features of that master. She pressed the child closer and kissed his smiling mouth. No! All was not lost. Hope was born anew and courage came to bear her company.

II

ALEXANDRIA

TWO years had passed. From her capital, whither she had returned crushed by the disaster of the Ides of March, Cleopatra was still watching the civil war which was destroying the Roman world. That violent struggle, which was led alternately by the murderers and the avengers of Cæsar, was a series of brutal reverses. The feeling that it roused in her was not merely one of sentiment. Grief for the great man who had loved her so passionately, the desire to see his vile assassins punished, were mixed with grave political anxiety.

For nearly a century Egypt had been impossible to govern. Restless, corrupt, sanguinary, it had become a prey to the various pretenders to the throne. To hold it together in any way, to utilize the magnificent resources of its rich soil, to get rid of the bands of pirates, deserters, and outlaws which made up the larger part of its army, required a stronger power than the Lagidæ possessed. Too indolent to make any exertion, these dilettante sovereigns had formed the habit of appealing to Rome for aid whenever a new insurrection broke out. Ptolemy the Piper, Cleopatra's father, had only been able to secure his crown by bribing the Roman

Senators; and as to Cleopatra, we know what means she had used to regain her sceptre!

If the peace that she had restored seemed desirable, if she had been given credit for the temporary prosperity of the country, there was also much discontent that these things had been accomplished at the price of a scandal, and by an alliance which, at any time, might change the ruling power and put it in foreign hands.

Feeling herself deserted, surrounded by opposition, by plots, deprived of the troops, which, owing to military reasons, had been removed to other parts, the Queen had days of deep depression. She was overwhelmed by her responsibilities, especially when her ministers came with various accounts: of a pest so terrible that the embalmers were unable to care for the bodies of the dead; with sickening tales of the corpses which lined the public highways; again of famine, which for two successive seasons had ravished the land; of the wasteful extravagance of dishonest officials in charge of government affairs; of the difficulties of administration which each and every day brought forth. She was weary and often went back in imagination to the days when the passion of a mighty conqueror had taken all care away, and she had only to wave her ivory sceptre to have any desire fulfilled.

What remained to-day of that ancient alliance? It was Rome now that stood in need of aid. Moreover, she was invoking it, and in the present state of discord each faction was, in turn, begging the support of Egypt's fleet. If Cleopatra did not respond to this appeal it was because she was uncertain which side would win. To which party would the Republic belong to-morrow? If the conspirators who had murdered Cæsar were victorious, it was probable that, shorn of power as it was, the kingdom of Egypt, together with those of Greece, Syria, Gaul, and Spain, as well as Mauritania, would become merely colonies of Rome. If the other party, that was loyal to Cæsar's memory, were the winner, then she could look for the consideration due her. Was it not likely that the friends of Cæsar, desirous of carrying on the work that he had planned, would guard the interests of the woman whom he had named as his wife? Would they not protect the child who bore his image? But who would be the conquerors? Cleopatra was tormented with the perpetual question; and the report of Cassius' success in Macedonia filled her with apprehension.

That was in the early autumn. Then came winter, with its fogs and storms; navigation was suspended and there was no further news from the battlefields.

The sight of Alexandria, filled as that city was for her with memories and with forebodings, plunged her into endless reveries. There the brimming cup of joy had been handed her and she had drunk her fill. Often at sunset, when the magic purple light bathed the landscape, she would climb to one of the terraces looking toward the Bruchium and gaze upon the façades of shimmering gold. How lovely it was, stretched under the fiery sky, at the edge of the tawny beach; or lighted at night by the giant torches of its watch-towers! How much more beautiful it had grown in the decades since its founder had drawn the first plans and shaped its boundaries, which lay around it like the folds of a military cloak. The Queen of such a city might well be proud. In whichever direction she looked were many-coloured marbles, enamelled domes of porcelain, triumphal arches, façades exquisitely carved. On the crest of a small hill stood the Pantheon, called in jest the Cage of the Muses. It was here, according to ancient tradition which the Lagidæ held in deepest reverence, that poets, sculptors, musicians, and artists of all nations were accorded a warm welcome, always provided they had excelled in their art and were faithful worshippers of Apollo.

Here, in the middle of the colonnade, stood the famous Library—rich, even after the terrible fire, in the possession of seven hundred thousand volumes, and which held, among other precious treasures, the Septimus, that first translation of the Bible into Greek, made by seventy-two learned Egyptian Jews, under Ptolemy Philadelphus. Not far distant, as though to seek the fountain of spiritual nourishment, clustered the group of temples of Serapis. This centre of learning, home of history, philosophy, medicine, and mathematics, as well as guardian of previous manuscripts, was in very truth the light of the world. To-day, after two thousand years, we are indebted to it for the preservation of the life of Greek literature.

The instruction given there, the names of the savants who taught, the methods employed, the accuracy of the instruments, the very quality of the papyrus furnished the students, all these were so justly famous that wealthy people of all countries, Rome, Athens, even distant Asia, who had some especially gifted son desired to send him there, that he might bear the illustrious seal of having been a student at Alexandria.

Across the distance, to the wide avenues where chariots, litters, cavalcades were thronging the broad streets, Cleopatra was still gazing. She saw the circuses, the theatres; the gymnasium, with the crowd at its doors, reading the announcements; the stadium, with its circling race-course; she looked at the gigantic hippodrome, which twenty thousand spectators could barely fill; at the widely scattered temples which over-topped the houses, dominating the other buildings by their mysterious grandeur, and farther on, she saw, with a thrill of awe, the Soma, that mausoleum where, in a crystal sarcophagus, rested the repatriated body of her heroic ancestor.

Of these precious stones, of all this magnificence, the Queen reckoned the worth, and with a fearful pride asked herself: "Will all this be mine tomorrow?" Her mind revelled in the vastness of her heritage; she regarded the inexhaustible valley, watered by the divine river; she thought of the thirty thousand towns which from north to south reared their noble ramparts; of Bubastos, where the goddess of love reigned; of Memphis, sleeping at the base of her pyramids; of Thebes, the Holy City; of Hermonthis, called the glory of two heavens; of Edfu, rich in antique treasures. Farther on, she saw, in imagination, those southern regions which produce granite and spices; the legendary vineyards, where each cluster of grapes was so heavy that two men were needed to carry it to the wine-press. She went back to that enchanted island whose perfumed paths bore the traces of her footsteps, near to those of her lover. Her old-time confidence returned and she cried: "No, my Egypt! sacred land of Osiris and of Ra, you who fill the granaries of the earth and reverently protect your dead! Garden of palms and of vines! Shore where the holy ibis seeks cooling drink, never shall you be a slave!"

And Cleopatra was right. Success was in sight. A decisive victory had just been gained by Cæsar's avengers. Pirates, escaped from Naxos, had brought the good tidings. Brutus, then Cassius, had been defeated in the plains of Philippi, and each had taken his life with the blade which their treacherous hands had plunged in the blood of their benefactor; thus was justice done.

Cleopatra took fresh courage. New light came into her life, overshadowed since that fatal morning in March. Although still wrapped in mist, the future was no longer an opaque and indistinguishable mass of blackness. A certain harmony prevailed between it and the past. Rome emerged from the gloom. Freed from the conspirators, she might once more become a valuable ally.

Meanwhile, the Queen, faithful to the tradition of her ancestors, who had squandered fortunes in amusing the populace, ordered elaborate entertainments, beginning with religious ceremonies, accompanied by sacrifices. Was it not fitting to give thank-offerings to the gods who had just punished the hateful perpetrators of that deadly crime?

The people of Alexandria welcomed every opportunity for a festival. If their city was famous for its university, for the learned men who came there daily to give lectures, it was also a centre of dissipation; rich in every variety of entertainment, vibrating with the sheer joy of living. The enormous fortunes which were made there had produced unlimited luxury. For gaiety of all kinds, banquets, dances, races, theatres, orgies of love and wine, it was without a rival.

The fame of the Alexandrian festivals was far-spread. Wherever they were announced, at Bubastos, or at Pelusium, along the Syrian or Cilician coasts, eager throngs came to mingle with the populace. From day-break, along the broad promenades of the modern quarters, as well as in the overgrown alleys of the old Rhakotis, there were swarms of noisy people.

The many-coloured costumes, the variety of complexions, dark and fair, olive and amber, indicated the hurly-burly of the cosmopolitan town. The active life of its harbour, filled with all sorts of beauty and splendour, from the Pillars of Hercules to the entrance of the Indus; the various spectacles, the museums, the fabulous Nile, where flower-laden barges went up and down day and night; the primitive debauchery, to which Greek culture had added every possible refinement, all these whetted curiosity and made the diversions of the metropolis inexhaustible.

On one hand a high-shouldered native, his loins girded with bright-coloured cloths, led an ass laden with leathern bottles; another was driving a wheat-cart; there, a sunburned, withered sailor dragged his net; yonder soldiers marched, whose imposing appearance attracted the crowd. Men from all countries and of all races were gathered together there.

Greeks predominated, recognizable, under their palliums, by their athletic suppleness; there were Romans with their bronze masks, and Gauls, whose blue eyes and close-fitting woollen tunics contrasted strangely with the heavy lidded Asiatics, whose flowing, embroidered robes swept the dust.

The different nationalities of the women were even more conspicuous, owing to their curious coiffures; some wore the hair loose, others made it into curls on either side of their cheeks; and still others, as the girls from Ephesus, fastened it with golden pins, intertwined with flowers and leaves.

Vast numbers of nomads, usually restricted to the suburbs, added to the throngs in the streets, for the police were ordered to be tolerant on the fête days. Save on the Royal Way, which was reserved exclusively for the official cortèges, Arabs were allowed to wander at will, leading, by a cord passed through a nose-ring, one or more camels, whose air of indescribable dignity dominated the crowd. There were Jews, who carried bags of money hidden in their shabby, black caftans; Ethiopians and Kaffirs, with baskets of figs and citrons balanced on their crimped heads.

Mingling in this mob, strolling about in couples, were lazy little working-girls, attracted by the claptrap inducements of fortune-tellers, watching the acrobats who, standing on their heads, swallowed swords; or pausing to gaze at the light and wiry jugglers leaping in and out of the encircling flames. There were loafers everywhere, seeking amusement; children in danger of being crushed by the crowd; even ladies of rank, who, diverted by the street-shows, had left their litters, and were closely followed by their slaves to protect them from being jostled.

But everyone had to contend with the general disorder and each was in danger of being hustled or even beaten down. Theocritus has left us a vivid sketch describing a scene at one of these popular festivals between two young women from Syracuse. One of them, Gorga, is visiting her friend. She arrives all out of breath.

"O Praxinoa! give me a chair, quick! Put a cushion in it. How my heart is thumping! I thought I never should find you. You live so far away, and what a crowd there is to get through!"

Praxinoa listened while she finished dressing. Her maid, Eunoe, brought her water, soap, and the key of her big chest. She took out a hat and dress and added the last touches to her costume.

Gorga: "How becoming the long, plaited effect of that dress is! Was it very expensive?"

Praxinoa: "Ah! don't speak of it! It cost more than two mines of pure silver, to say nothing of the time it took to make it up."

After some grumbling about their husbands, and instructions to the Phrygian attendant to look after the baby and to keep the dog shut up, the two women leave the house. As soon as the door is closed Praxinoa cried: "Ye gods, what a rabble! What shall we do? How can we walk? And here come the soldiers! Look at the cavalry! Nothing frightens me so much as horses. Gorga! Look at that chestnut mare kicking!"

Gorga: "Never mind, it's going back in line now!"

They push ahead through the surging crowd. But the sensitive Praxinoa is all confused. "Give me your hand," she calls to Gorga. "And Eunoe, you hold on to Eutyclus. Let us keep close together lest we lose each other."

In spite of these precautions they were soon forced apart by the mob. "How unlucky I am!" exclaimed Praxinoa; her pretty plaited dress had been trodden under foot by a passing man. She called angrily after him: "By Jupiter, be careful if you don't want me to. . . ."

But the offender was a gallant man. Instead of being rude he apologized and helped Praxinoa to arrange her disordered gown. "Take courage, lady, you are out of danger now!" Praxinoa thanked him, with the gratitude of a person who has just been rescued: "Kindly stranger, how can I express my appreciation of your help and protection?" Just here she caught sight of Gorga, and the two friends fell into each other's arms.

"I have been looking everywhere for you, Gorga!"

"And I for you, Praxinoa!" they proceeded to discuss their mishaps.

Praxinoa: "See, my dress is all torn!"

Gorga: "So is my cloak. What will my husband say?"

Arm in arm they walked along the road to the edge of the Bruchium where the banquet is being prepared.

"Is it much farther?" they demanded of an old woman.

"Alas, yes, my children!"

"At least it will be an easy matter to get in?"

The old woman, who knew her Homer, teased them: "'With strenuous efforts the Greeks entered Troy.' If you take enough trouble, my fair maids, you may reach your goal!"

* * *

There was a sudden flourish of trumpets. It was the signal for the procession to start. It filed by, solemn, unending, with the musicians at its head, half-naked cymbal players clanging their shining disks; cithern players, who sounded rings strung on metal threads; men, striking with sycamore sticks the wild asses' skins stretched over round drums hanging from their necks.

At a certain distance, intended to indicate the difference between them and what was merely human, the cortège of priests appeared. The trumpet players had already commanded silence and with reverent interest the spectators gazed at the horoscope casters, who could reveal the future; the hieroglyphic readers; prophets with long beards, who burned incense in little brass boxes; priests, whose duty it was to offer to faithful worshippers the images of the gods. Raising their gilded staffs, some would balance the standards by their painted ends; others, accompanied them in chariots; amid the general exultation, and before the staring eyes of the crowd, filed the mysterious figures of Apis, Hathor, the Bull; of the grimacing Toth, of Horus, in his sparrow-hawk mask, of Anubis, the god of Death, all expressing unknown power. There were great shoutings and cries as these images passed, for all believed in the might of this blind matter, all believed in its power of conferring an infinite degree of strength on the suppliant.

Between two rows of soldiers the High Priest at last was seen advancing. He was a very old man and leaned on a cane. A long, hyacinth-coloured veil covered his hands and his face, which no profane glance was allowed to desecrate. He alone was admitted to private conference with the god, who presently, through his mouth, would reveal the oracle. After him came the priestesses, young, pure, dressed entirely in white, their pointed fingers balancing the stems of lotus-flowers. Then followed the conjurers, with their quivering torches; the bell ringers; the bird catchers, who, on their batons daubed with glue, held the sacred fowls. Then came the beggars, exposing their infirmities; the vendors of sacred images, of scarabs, of amulets; the inevitable commercial tail that always drags behind wherever man raises up a god to be adored. And all this tide of incongruous beings, this turbulent collection of races, of passions, of divers interests, advanced in order, marching with even step toward the fascinating goal, which yonder against the azure sky, resplendent and sacred, called to them all alike to come: the temple of Serapis.

Built on the model of the old temples of the gods, this sanctuary, uniting all forms of worship, was the most noted in Egypt. The princely sums with which it was endowed served continually to augment its power, and only the most famous monuments of the Roman Capitol could compare with its mighty structure. One hundred steps led up to the entrance. Its portal was guarded by a line of sphinxes of imposing majesty; and along its sides, from arches of yellow and vermilion, light streamers floated in the wind.

As they approached the entrance the students of the different colleges took their places along the portico, according to their rank. Some stood in the empty spaces between the rows of columns and, thus, little by little, the building was filled, peopled with human forms which, in their immobility, resembled groups of statues.

Suddenly there was a commotion. Everyone turned toward a light which shone above the crowd. A herald announced "The Queen!" Magnificent, surrounded by a glittering guard, on her way, one would have said, to a heavenly kingdom, Cleopatra appeared, borne on a shield. Seeing her thus, so innocent, in a sheath of silver which encircled her as though she were a graven image, with her knees bent, her elbows close to her sides, her eyes raised to the sky, it was not possible to believe the evil tales about her. She was no longer the woman, but the august daughter of kings; a priestess, who, in another moment, would be in the presence of a god. Four slaves waved immense fans of peacocks' feathers above her head, and at her feet, like a cushion, a panther lay.

While the temple slaves attended to the slaughter of the victims, whose warm entrails were smoking on the slope, a young poet-singer, his zither hanging from his shoulder, advanced and, after bowing to the multitude, began chanting the praises of the Queen. *"Thy hair is like a sweet-smelling plant. Thy hands are the palms of love. Thy brow is like a moon coming out from behind a cloud. Thine eyes, with their shining lashes, are two summer butterflies. Thy teeth have the brilliancy of a stream, running between two banks bordered with roses and peonies."* And after each verse, a chorus of virgins would take up the refrain: *"Hail to thee, O resplendent daughter of Amoun-Ra!"*

The moment for the burnt-offerings had come. Erect now, her shoulders covered with the mantle of Isis, white as wheat, followed by the priests and the chief dignitaries, Cleopatra stepped over the sill of the temple, and the enormous door, behind which crouched the terrifying watch-dog of granite, with his triple head of wolf, jackal, and lion, was closed. In the farthest corner, behind great columns, covered with hieroglyphics explaining the destiny of the human soul, stood a Serapis of marble and of gold. Ruling deity in whom was combined the antique Kronos, together with the Zeus of the Greeks and the Jupiter of the Latins, Serapis was the national god. He was believed to be omnipotent. It was to him that the Egyptians looked for glory, health, and riches; from him came their faith in the mighty powers of the waters of the Nile. His figure was three times the height of man and serene majesty was written on his features. His beard spread over his knees, abundant and shining; the seal of kings was on his forehead; his hands were extended with a gesture that seemed to embrace the whole world. By a skilful arrangement the light, coming in from above, fell on his enamelled lips, and this single ray produced the effect of a kiss from heaven, and gave his worshippers the illusion that he was speaking.

Before this colossal statue the sacrificial table was spread. The signs of the Zodiac were engraved on its huge circumference. In the centre was burning oil, and side by side with the blood of the victims were precious vases holding wine and wheat, the water of the Nile, and the seven perfumes most agreeable to the god. While the High Priest inclined toward the flame, pouring out the offerings that the fire might devour them, the Queen prostrated herself before the altar. She pleaded, she implored: "O mighty god, all-powerful god, whom the winds obey, be favourable to my prayers. Liberate thy healing waters, let their abundance flow over Egypt and make her fertile. Let no sedition breed in her cities, nor alien enemy come to destroy her troops. May her people be loyal to her and protect her with foot-soldiers armed with arrows, and with horsemen in shining armour."

Absorbed in the mysterious rites in the temple, all hearts were beating furiously. It was the moment when the omens would become visible; and, as though a single soul, a single voice, the multitude united in the prayer of its sovereign. Moved by an unconquerable faith she repeated the words of supplication: "O mighty god, god whom the winds obey, liberate the still waters!"

The smoke cleared away, the cedar doors of the temple reopened, and the Queen reappeared. She was very pale. Under her sparkling necklaces her bosom was heaving. Her large eyes were gazing far off, beyond earthly things, into that region of prophecy whither her prayer had ascended. What had she seen there? What had she heard? What communication from the oracle did the High Priest have to bring? Three blasts of the trumpet announced that the Queen was about to speak. She came to the edge of the first step, and her voice, sweet as a flute, pronounced these words:

"May the name of Serapis be praised! His mercy is upon us. He promises glory and prosperity to Egypt. On your seed the Nile will spread her blessed waters and will make your wheat to swell!"

A tremendous clamour arose. From the thousands of throats it swelled like the roar of a hurricane. With enthusiasm, with an almost insane gratitude, as though the miracle had already taken place, thanks began to pour forth.

With a gesture like that of Neptune when he bids the floods be still, the Queen commanded silence. She had not yet finished speaking.

"The goodness of Serapis," she said, "surpasses our hopes. He loves Egypt; he wishes for it greatness and prosperity. From him will come a warrior whose sword cannot know defeat."

A new burst of enthusiasm arose, which this time nothing could suppress. It was a general delirium, a reaching out toward joy, toward that great unknown happiness which the mass as well as the individual expects from the future.

The shield was again lowered. The Queen climbed up lightly, barely touching the three ivory steps of the wooden stool, then, with the fans waving above her head, the panther crouching at her feet, she took again the road leading to the palace. Shouts, flowers, and palms greeted her on every side, but she did not seem to see any of these things.

Lost in a world of thought, she was dreaming her own dreams. However skeptical she might have felt, she had been impressed by the words of the High Priest. Would a warrior really come? And if he did, who would he be? A name came to her mind. With curious persistence, past memories began to fill her fancy. Some details, almost forgotten, came back to her. One evening, nearly three years before, in the villa on the banks of the Tiber;

the conversation between Cæsar and Trebonius had grown dull. The question had come up as to whether the committees would meet again or be abolished from the concourse. Suddenly the door was flung open and Mark Antony entered. It was a new life that came in. He was laughing; his hair fell over his forehead; his shoulders, cut like those of his ancestor, Hercules, were strong enough to carry the Nemean lion. His presence impregnated the atmosphere of the room with youth, with warm, glowing exuberance, and straightway Cleopatra had felt his covetous eyes fall on her, with that look which a woman always understands. How often since that first evening she had felt that same look, that frank admission on the part of the man that he was no longer master of himself. And another evening, when they had been left alone for a moment, she had felt the warm touch of his lips on her shoulder. Her surprise and embarrassment had been so great that, wishing to conceal them, she had sought refuge in flight. Since then he had been more reserved; but if he did not speak, if his manner were constrained, it was because his loyalty to Cæsar had put a seal upon his lips. How would he have dared do otherwise? And Cleopatra, though fully aware of his feeling, how would she have received an avowal of his love? Undoubtedly Cæsar's exalted position restrained his inferior officer, who owed everything to him, from trespassing on forbidden ground; just as it prevented Cleopatra from yielding to any passing fancy. However tempting the athletic beauty of Mark Antony, glory was her chief ambition. She would let nothing stand in the way of that. But to-day death had changed everything. Mark Antony stood in Cæsar's place; he had no master for a rival. Could it be that he was the saviour whom the god had promised?

Weary of her widowhood, a flood of hope, at this thought, swept over her heart. She wanted to be alone to give herself up to these dreams.

The sun had just set, and a crescent of silver was visible in the evening sky. One by one the high lamps, planted like trees along the avenues, shone out. Delicate, rose-coloured illuminations began to sparkle along the edges of the houses, where they hung like fruit among the thin branches of the plane trees. If the festivals of the daylight had been rich and attractive, the evening decorations satisfied the sensuous taste. The Queen had given orders that no expense be spared to give general pleasure. The fountains at the palace doors ran red with wine, and on the long tables in the inner courts, which led from the stables to the kitchen, meats, pastries, and cheese were served to the public. Order was carefully preserved and, after getting their portions, the people were compelled to move on. Many went to the theatres, where free performances were given; others preferred to linger by the street-shows, watching the farces; others wound up the evening's entertainment in some of the notorious resorts of the Rhakotis.

While the common people amused themselves thus, herded together in an atmosphere of dust and sweat, the rich people, to whom every day was a holiday, entertained themselves in a less vulgar manner. Many, at the hour of supper, left the crowded part of the city to linger along the aristocratic avenues on the west side of the great capital, which seemed half asleep among their silent gardens.

A group of perfumed dandies stopped before a dwelling, small, but of charming proportions, surrounded by pine trees. A slave came out to open the gate. Crossing the vestibule, where a fountain was playing, they were introduced into a hall lined from floor to ceiling by thousands of rolls of papyrus. It was the library where Polydemus, who had made a fortune in perfumes, delighted to receive his guests. Those whom he had invited this evening belonged to various circles of society; for it was his pleasure that in his home all subjects should be discussed and all the topics of the day be passed upon freely. Except in art, where he had a preference for the Greek style, he was liberal-minded, and so unprejudiced that he did not hesitate to bring together men of opposing views. Consequently he numbered among his guests Apollodorus, the secretary of the Queen, whose devotion to her was well known; Demetrius, the lieutenant, who had fought him under Achillas; Sati, a Theban of ancient family, who was wedded to the old traditions and objected to all foreign influence; rhetoricians, noted for their Athenian culture; financiers and artists; philosophers, as little likely to hold the same views on any one subject as are men of political bent.

Behind drawn curtains the hall was brilliantly lighted. Between the delicate columns, busts of Homer, Pindar, Zeno, and Epicurus rested on bronze pedestals; and, alternating with them, as though to thank these great men for their indulgence, stood graceful statues of women.

The guests reclined on couches, placed around a table which was adorned with silver and painted pottery. In the middle stood an alabaster bowl, surrounded by branches of rose-bushes, some of which, as though too heavy to bear their own weight, fell in garlands on the snow-white table-cover. As soon as the banqueters were comfortably settled the first course was served. Eels from Lake Mareotis, just outside Alexandria, covered with a sauce flavoured with caraway seed; congers, fried in butter; roe, in tiny casseroles.

Then began the general conversation, trivial at first, turning on the happenings of the day. One guest commented on the passing processions, which had never been better managed; another on the sumptuous banquets which were being served at the Bruchium; this one praised the marvellous circus, where two hundred beasts and twenty gladiators had been slaughtered; that one called the attention of the guests to the wonderful illuminations which, seen through the open windows, were reddening the skies above the city.

Apollodorus took advantage of these various comments to dwell upon the gracious generosity of the Queen, who was always eager to afford happiness to her people.

"Hail to Cleopatra!" responded the artists, who were being entertained in the halls of the Paneum.

"Hail to the beloved of the gods!"

"Glory to her who is a delight to our eyes!"

"Drink to her who brings light to our minds!"

But, as always, this very praise aroused controversy. If the young Queen had passionate admirers, especially among the younger men who, impressed by her beauty and intelligence, were led to expect great things, there were others, grave and sedate men, who were shocked by her audacity. From the time of her liaison with Cæsar they had criticized her lack of dignity. There were even suspicions in regard to the recent death of her young brother, and hostile queries as to what part she might have had in it.

This evening the wanton extravagance of the present fêtes came under discussion, and the air was full of unfriendly criticism. It was no time to spend money recklessly when a severe famine was devastating the land. Some, who had noticed certain affectations of taste and manner, which Cleopatra had shown since her return from Italy, were fierce in their condemnation of her.

That very day, disdainful of the old ceremony with the Pschent, surmounted by the sacred Uræus, a ceremony at which kings and queens from time immemorial had covered their hair with the ancient headdress, Cleopatra had substituted a diadem! And on that ornament, which concealed her temples and forehead, the respecters of the old Egyptian tradition had been horrified to see the image of Minerva instead of that of Isis, worn by her who was supposed to be the priestess of Isis.

Sati deplored these conditions. "It is the first time that a sovereign of ours has treated an ancient custom with contempt!"

When the sculptor Nicias remarked that this diadem, which revealed the nape of her neck, was most becoming to her delicate profile, the venerable Theban rebuked him:

"So far from favouring them the Queen should be the first to discourage these foreign fashions."

This objection was not surprising from a man who still wore the old national tunic, held in place by a belt with floating ends, and whose curled beard reached nearly to his waist.

Apollodorus observed smilingly that it seemed scarcely worth while to lay so much stress on the matter of a coiffure.

The subject, unluckily, was not so trivial as the devoted secretary wished to represent. He was not unaware of the state of things, and in these criticisms he saw plainly the attitude of those who, having suffered from the effects of the Roman invasion, were all too ready to reproach the Queen for having brought it about. He desired in every way to lay stress on her loyalty to her people.

Unfortunately, the former lieutenant of Achillas chose that moment to recall all that the invasion had cost Egypt: two years of war, the destruction of the fleet, a great part of their priceless library wiped out by fire. . . .

The latter memory was particularly painful to the thoughtful men, for they loved books and naturally deplored the irreparable loss of their country's treasures. Was this splendid banquet to turn to vinegar in their mouths?

As though pricked by a spur Polydemus turned the talk to other subjects. Pointing to the satinwood shelves, where lay thousands of rolls of papyrus, he announced that he was leaving them in his will to the city of Alexandria, and that there were many rare copies among them of which he was the sole possessor, and that these would replace the specimens which had been so unfortunately destroyed by fire.

This generous gift was warmly appreciated. The friends of this good citizen congratulated him on his public spirit, and unanimously expressed the hope that the promised legacy would not come to them for many years.

The second course of the banquet was now served. A huge copper basin was brought in, containing a whole sheep, whose flesh was still crackling; then come a platter, embellished with various dressings, on which was a giant goose still decked in his coat of feathers, whose stomach was stuffed with snipe. These delicacies were carved in the twinkling of an eye, the guests who were nearest the host being served first. They used silver spatula and chiselled spoons. The light from the flaring torches made the table shine like gold. The perfume of the roses was so strong that the food seemed flavoured with it. For a few moments the guests were absorbed in the consumption of the epicurean delicacies and silence reigned. There was no sound save the flitting steps of the slaves as they passed to and fro.

Suddenly one of the slaves announced that a vessel had just entered the harbour, with an important messenger on board. Just what his errand was no one as yet knew, in fact, nothing would be known until the next day. There were, however, grave rumours, and serious happenings were said to be going on at Rome. A shiver ran around the table. The Egyptians, always suspicious concerning Rome and her schemes, already felt the entangling meshes of the net which perhaps in another twenty-four hours would hold them captives. What might this news be? What horrors, what scandals, were yet in store? For the past two years the Forum had been nothing more than a nest of bandits, and the echo of its evil brawls was constantly in their ears.

Polydemus, anxious that there should be no second disturbance at his supper, expressed the hope that with the triumph of the Cæsarian party an era of peace and order would be established. But there was an outcry from his guests. What order, what justice could be expected from people who, although fighting for the same cause, had never ceased to destroy each other? No one referred to Lepidus; his very mediocrity protected him from criticism. But what of Antony? Of Octavius? Which of these was the greater villain? In the hubbub of noisy speeches each gave himself up to reciting the various sensational acts which witnesses, or writers, had handed on to him.

"While performing his sacred duties a priest was told he was to be banished and sought refuge," said Eudoxos. "Too late! Before he could cross the sill of the Tribunal, a centurion stabbed him."

Lycon declared that mothers, to save themselves, shut their doors against their own sons who were suspected of treason; that daughters did not hesitate to tell where their fathers were concealed.

Even little children, according to another, were

no longer safe. One child, on its way to school, had been seized by an executioner and slaughtered before the eyes of its parents.

"Remember, above all else, the brutal assassination of Cicero," cried the rhetorician, Antipus, who had made a journey to Rome expressly to hear the voice of that great orator.

"That was an unpardonable crime," agreed one of his colleagues, "and it will leave a lasting stain on the name of Mark Antony!"

Apollodorus, who the moment before had been praising the latter, in order to protect the Queen, now tried to throw the odium of this assassination on Octavius. He was chiefly to blame; the friend of Cicero, he, like a white-livered coward, and without a single qualm, had given Cicero into the hands of the murderers. He whom, only a few days before, Cicero had pressed to his heart and called his son!

A shiver of disgust ran around the table as though a serpent had appeared in the room. Again the talk turned on Mark Antony. In spite of his misdoings, he at least, with the coarse tunic that he put on when he went to drink with the soldiers and the women of the town, with his sword slung over his shoulder and his chariot drawn by lions, accompanied by the courtesan Cytheris, was amusing. A voice was even heard praising him, for a brave man will always find someone to stand up for him.

The philosopher, Lycon, though a professed cynic, recalled that at the moment when the conspirators were still waving their swords, when Octavius was in hiding, and when terror prevailed throughout

Rome, Mark Antony had had the courage to insist on a proper funeral for Cæsar and had stood before the body of his benefactor and fearlessly proclaimed his virtues.

But this praise aroused little enthusiasm. The group of distinguished men of letters had no interest in a boor like Antony whose valour was simply that of the battle-field.

The diatribe that the sculptor Nicias hurled against the Romans met the popular sentiment. If the invasion of these barbarians continued, what would become of the present civilization? He had just come from Corinth and knew that many of the splendid buildings had already been destroyed. Greece was a mass of ruins. What was to be expected if these things continued?

The supper was over at last. The creams and pastries gave forth a delicious odour of wild honey. The citrons were all the more refreshing after the highly spiced dishes of the repast. The rare wines had increased in exquisite bouquet with each course. After the cider and mead, the delicate, violet-flavoured wines of Phœnicia were served, then the warm liqueurs of Spain. There were also the celebrated Gallic wines, clear and sparkling, well calculated to drive away all manner of depression.

The conversation turned on women. It was not usual for them to be absent from the banquets at Polydemus's house; but this evening, those that he had invited, chiefly celebrated courtesans, for he was unmarried, had had engagements elsewhere. The younger men, who were devoted to horse-racing, had taken Faustina and Leah to the stadium to see their horses run. Chloris could not leave Naudres, that noted actor, on the evening when, shod with buskins and with trumpet-like voice, he played his famous rôle of Orestes; a banquet at Gauthene's had attracted Moussaria and Trophena, for they knew that the two sons of the banker Rupin would be there as well as the heir of the richest ship-owner of Ephesus. A number had preferred to keep their evening free that they might stroll along the Heptastadium, for a night such as this afforded every chance of meeting open-handed gallants.

The older men agreed that a supper was fully as agreeable without women, and Sati declared that their presence was often a drawback to interesting conversation.

"Is that on account of their modesty?" inquired Lycias, who loved his joke.

"They cannot talk of anything but love," sighed the banker in a bored tone.

The poet, Melanis, who up to then had said nothing, raised his voice in protest. "Even though the hour and place were not especially consecrated to love, was it not permissible to evoke its charming images?" he demanded.

"For my part," declared the lieutenant, "I don't think there's any sense in discussing such things."

Just at that moment, the cup-bearer appeared, bringing, with great care, an amphora. It contained a marvellous Cyprian wine, one of those rare vintages which the lips approach with reverence. Many of the men declared that nothing so delicious had ever tickled their palates.

"O wine! Golden fountain that reflects the sun! Flagon that the generous gods have spilled on the earth to rejoice the hearts of men!" exclaimed the young Melanis, in a burst of improvisation.

Taking advantage of the general good humour that the wine had created, Apollodorus reminded the company that if Cyprus were once more a province of Egypt, and if its wines came into Alexandria free of duty, it was to Cleopatra that they owed the credit.

"That is very true," said Polydemus. "The restoration of this province was really a gift from Cæsar to the Queen."

This reference to the wine produced a spirit of good-will, and those who had been criticizing Cleopatra most severely now raised their glasses in her honour, and the master of the house was pleased to see the supper, which angry arguments had several times threatened to spoil, end in good humour.

About eleven o'clock the slaves withdrew and the dancers, with attendant musicians, appeared under the peristyle. They were twelve young girls of pure Egyptian descent, whose type is still preserved and known to us to-day as the Gypsy.

At the sound of the five-stringed lyre their lithe bodies began to sway. The figures that they formed, first approaching, then retreating, turning to join hands and then withdraw again, were not so much a dance, as a game between nymphs and their pursuing satyrs. This first movement was soon succeeded by livelier frolics. Tambourines and castanets resounded. The legs of the dancers, which until then had only bent and moved gracefully, had an irresistible impetus. At the same moment black eyes shot lightning glances from under blue-white lids; there was a wave of sound, heels clicked, and rings clanged together. A whirl of bare flesh was visible through the slit tunics, bent-over backs straightened up, arms, interlaced like branches, unwound themselves abruptly.

Now delightfully voluptuous, now urged on by the wild music, the dancing continued far into the night. The older men, stupefied by the heavy meal and the abundant flow of wine, soon grew drowsy; but the younger ones, who had been somewhat bored during the long-drawn-out repast, were now waked to feverish excitement. With a kind of intoxication they followed the women's gestures, which seemed to parody love before their eyes, making it waver, come forward, then, in a flash, rise and triumph in an ecstatic embrace.

The roses were fading in the alabaster vases. The torches, one by one, flickered and went out. The pale dawn was creeping through the parted curtains, as the banqueters took leave of their gracious host, expressing appreciation of his kindly hospitality.

Apollodorus, whose duties at the Bruchium began very early, had no time to return to his own home, which was far out on the road toward Sais. There was a chance, however, for him to walk off the last fumes of the Cyprian wine.

The city was deserted. Silence reigned, but the flagstones seemed still vibrating from the tread of countless feet. Here and there lay withered garlands, side by side with various lost objects, bits of draggled silk and other débris, which had been part of the evening's vanities. The abandoned halls, these cast-off trifles, brought a certain sadness to Apollodorus as he recalled the discussions at Polydemus's table. They were rebellious, dissatisfied, hard to control, these subjects of Cleopatra, and how evident was the feeling of enmity against her. There were parties ready at any moment to band together and bring about one of those revolutions which her ancestors had ceaselessly combated; and what countless traps had already been set for her! He remembered the day when he sailed in a fishing boat to seek her on the beach at Canopus. But then a mighty power sheltered her, worked for her. To-day, alone, criticized on every side, opposed, would she have sufficient strength? . . .

His mind filled with these misgivings, Apollodorus found himself at the door of the palace. In the misty morning light, the delicate architecture, with its multitude of supporting columns, seemed almost aërial. He was astounded to see the Queen standing on one of the terraces. Her hair was loosened and her scarf was waving in the breeze. He learned that just as her women were preparing her for bed a courier had arrived and she had had a long conference with him. At its close she had shown keen delight. "There are times when life is too beautiful to lose any moment of it in sleep," she had said when her attendants had begged her to rest for a while. Left alone, she had unrolled the script which confirmed the message that had just come to her.

The tidings recorded were so many and so unexpected that she was compelled to go over them two or three times, and then to repeat them to herself. This much, at least, was true: reconciled by their victory, the avengers of Cæsar had formed a new Triumvirate. The world was in their hands. They had divided it, or rather, Mark Antony, the only champion to fight and conquer Octavius (who, ill and quaking in his tent, had awaited him with chattering teeth) had divided it, according to his own liking. He gave the control of barbarous Gaul and a part of Italy, ruined and still racked by threats of revolution, to his wretched associate; Lepidus, who had not even taken any part in the war, had Spain (which was always on the eve of insurrection) and the African provinces assigned to him; and Mark Antony, supreme arbitrator and the worshipped leader of thirty-two legions, the hero before whom all knees were bent, claimed for his share of the spoils the mighty Orient, always desired, always coveted on account of its riches.

So, the words of the god had not been in vain. The sacred promise had been fully carried out. She, Cleopatra, would have an ally as powerful as Cæsar, and one whom she would have chosen above all others.

As things now stood all lay within her grasp. The past had taught her that a woman like herself could make of such a man, of such a great man, whatever she desired. Was not this the moment to put her experience to the test, to try with another that fortune which before had played her false? The flood of hope rose quickly. It came from the depths of her being, like a magic stream, washing away her grief in a single wave. The future, full of beautiful vistas, spread out before her. The walls of her room seemed to cramp her vision and she went out on the terrace. Night was almost gone. A mist of silver floated between the sea and sky. A sudden light gleamed through the haze, the horizon was transfused with rose-coloured clouds, and through the limpid light shot the gold and scarlet rays of the rising sun.

III

Mark Antony

IN THE accounts written by the admirers of Cæsar Augustus, Mark Antony is depicted as a combination of all the vices. His adversaries undoubtedly had good grounds for denouncing a man whose name reeked of scandals and whose passions had driven him to fight against his own country. It is easy to see how conservative men would have taken exception to his free ways, his bragging, his notorious wine-drinking, his extravagant habits; his gold plates carried, along with his mistresses, his mimes, and buffoons, into his very camps during the wars; the lions that were harnessed to his chariot, all the eccentricities which had caused him to be described as "an overgrown child who might have conquered the world and who did not know how to deny himself the least pleasure."

On the other hand, what charming characteristics he had, which they ignored! Without these delightful qualities, this foundation, so to say, which shone through the deceptive masquerade, how can we understand the continuous, irresistible attraction which he possessed for everyone who came in contact with him? People attract, not by the virtues that they strive for, but by their own natural charm.

Mark Antony was blessed with this magnetism. Superb in face and figure, a nobleman full of enthusiasm, whose gay spirits were contagious, brutal perhaps, at times, but never malicious, he possessed all the gifts to make life a thing of joy for himself and for those about him. He was noted for his generosity and his friends knew that they could appeal to it and did not hesitate to do so. On one occasion, Curion, a man of gay life like himself, being in sudden need of money to pay a gambling debt, came to him early one morning before he had finished dressing. Antony was in exactly the same predicament, having lost his last penny at the gaming table the night before. The two friends were dismayed. What could be done? They were out in the country at some distance from Rome and the need was pressing. How could they procure the necessary funds? Antony looked about him. The furnishings, the weapons, the skins of wild beasts, nothing had any money value. Suddenly his eyes lighted on a gold basin filled with water for his morning toilet. With a quick movement he emptied it. "There," he said, "take that. The goldsmith will certainly give you two talents for it."*

Though he spent money recklessly, he never used evil means to get it. Even Cicero, his mortal enemy, who brought many charges against him, did him the justice to say: "No one can accuse Mark Antony of dishonesty in money matters, of selfishness, or of any meanness of that kind."

In spite of his lax morals and of his deplorable

---

* NOTE: In Plutarch's "Life of Antony" a like incident is related of Antony's father.

habit of hard drinking, Antony was not lacking in nobility. It was his enemy, Seneca, who recognized this and described him: *Magnum virum ingenii nobilis.* And what finer keynote to his character as a man could be found than his loyal submission to his chief, whose glory he never coveted? As long as Cæsar lived, his young comrade-in-arms recognized that his own place was in the second rank. He never had any idea of usurping Cæsar's power, and aspired to his place only when he had Octavius for a rival.

It was chiefly on the battle-field that his real character was shown. Patient, steady, imperturbable, a model both of endurance and of submission to discipline, Antony won universal admiration. His soldiers, who had seen him in dangerous crises, would have followed him to the ends of the earth. They looked on him as a god. A man of Antony's temperament naturally had violent reactions. The more he had been restrained, the more he demanded when he was free. During the heroic retreat from Modena he slept on the hard ground, drank stagnant water, lived on roots and herbs; but when it was over, and peace was declared, the high-liver demanded his rights, and the orgies he held were not exceeded by Silenus himself. Just as moderation is the safe rule for most men, Antony thrived on excess. From every fatigue, from every indulgence, he came forth stronger, more keenly alive, invigorated.

Nature, with all her generous gifts to this grandson of Jupiter and Semele, had, however, denied him the one thing needful, without which the others were practically useless: Mark Antony had no commonsense. How could he have made great decisions? His passions were so compelling that he was carried away by them before he had time to reflect. They were irresistible, bearing him on with the force of a hurricane which is appeased only after having devastated all that lies in its path. Two elements fought for mastery in his ardent yet weak spirit: ambition and sensuality. Each, in turn supreme, carried him to extremes. Ambition, preeminent in his youth, had inspired those valorous deeds which had made him a leader in the invasions of Gaul and Sicily, and at the death of Cæsar had rendered him all-powerful in subduing the conspirators; between two campaigns it had led him to follow in Alexander's path and undertake the conquest of Persia. But sensuality was the stronger and conquered him at last. Little by little it took possession of its noble prey, binding him, engrossing all his faculties, stifling them, one by one, and at the end throwing him into the abyss of despair.

The morning after the battle of Philippi, before he had set foot on the soil of that Orient which was to be his triumph and his undoing, Antony was well balanced. Though his senses were exultant, his mind was filled with mighty projects. As he left that wild Macedonian country, where victory had been gained only after cruel sacrifices, the memory of whose bitter cold still made him shiver, he dreamed of those sunny southern lands, with their warmth and abundance, which his valour had won. Which one should he visit first? Each had its own attraction, each shore held some new charm. On the other side of Ossa and Pelion, whose snow-capped summits shut him in, lay the fascination and culture of Greece; beyond that, the coast of Asia, crowded with cities, each richer and more famous than the other: Smyrna, Ephesus, Pergamus; then Syria, with her palm trees, her gardens filled with luscious fruits; Lebanon, the stopping-place of the caravans from the Far East, laden with silks and precious stones. Then Palestine, arid beneath her gray olive trees, but crowned by holy Jerusalem, that sacred shrine calling a perpetual pilgrimage of Jews from the four corners of the earth; and above all, Egypt, Egypt fragrant with incense and violets, the kingdom of the incomparable Cleopatra!

Ever since the catastrophe of the Ides of March had so abruptly separated them, Antony had dreamed of the beautiful Queen. Often, in the heat of battle, or during the dreary watches in his tent at night, he had conjured up her fair image. Sometimes he saw again that indefinable look with which, when quite sure that she was unobserved, the mistress of Cæsar had returned his passionate regard. Tender and enticing, her glance, which stole toward him from between her long, dark lashes, seemed to demand his adoration. So vivid had been his sensations that at moments he was thrilled by the memory. The unspoken words of those evenings at the Transtevera would come back to him and, with the hunger of unsatisfied desire, he went over those scenes again and again. Unceasingly he repeated to himself the comforting thought that what had been impossible to him in the lifetime of Cæsar, he was no longer barred from taking. Cleopatra was free, and he, in his turn, had become one of the pillars of the world, a man whom any woman, even were she a queen, would be proud to call her lord. Above all, he had that magic gift of youth, to which all things are possible, and that ever-buoyant hope which, dreaming of the fairest fortune that the future may hold, whispers: "Why should not this be mine?"

But Antony was tormented by one ever-recurring doubt: what did Cleopatra really feel in regard to him? She had always been most gracious in her manner, but discreet at all times, careful not to give Cæsar the least ground for jealousy. What had she thought of him that day when, alone together for a moment, he had not been able to resist kissing her exquisite bare shoulder? She seemed like a beautiful sphinx, as, without remonstrance, without a smile, she had turned away and silently left the room. Was it love of the great Cæsar that made her so prudent, or the fear of losing his powerful protection? He had never understood her complex personality; he could not forget her feline grace, and those eyes which had stirred his innermost depths and had left him wondering, as does the mysterious beauty of a night in spring. What had she been doing for the past two years? He was utterly ignorant of her life, of her interests, and he longed to see her once more.

Antony, however, was not yet entirely in the power of these desires. The duties and responsibilities of his position were the chief factors in his life. He was fully alive to the necessity of visiting the new provinces that had come under his care, of giving them the protection which they had a right to expect from him. What excuse did he have for going first to Egypt? It was not, strictly speaking, a Roman province and could well afford to wait. Besides, it was not a good season for crossing.

So Antony sailed for Greece. It was not his first visit to that noble country. He had already trod the fields of Thessaly when, as a young commander, he had opposed Pompey. He had seen the wonderful temples of Delphi, Corinth, Olympia, with their wealth of sculpture and incomparable jewels. He had lingered in the forest of Eleusis, and in the theatre of Epidaurus he had been transported in spirit to the prophetic realms of the art of Æschylus. How thrilling it would be to revisit all these scenes! To come to them, clothed in majesty and with unlimited power!

The Greeks had become accustomed to foreign rule and no longer hated their conquerors. Indeed they had a certain regard for this Roman soldier who was said to be as handsome as Alcibiades and comparable to Themistocles in his warlike virtues. Among a people who counted physical strength and beauty as the highest gifts the gods could bestow, this son of Hercules had every chance of winning all hearts. He was welcomed graciously according to the custom of the country. The villages sent groups of men, bearing branches by day and torches by night, to escort his litter. As he entered the cities young girls greeted him with showers of roses, and a chorus of young men sang and danced to the music of lyres.

These acclamations were accompanied by alternate petitions and songs of praise. Wishing to prove how worthy he was of the latter, he showed his characteristic generosity in granting the requests. Ten thousand talents were donated to restore the theatre at Megara; at Thebes and Larissa he rebuilt the dwellings which Pompey's hordes had burned; and at Corinth he restored the ancient temple devoted to the worship of Venus Pandenus. While thus scattering gold broadcast he quickened his march over the slopes of Hymettus, for beyond them lay Athens, and he was eager to hear her honey-sweet praises.

Although badly damaged by Sulla's troops, pillaged by the greedy government which had succeeded him, poverty-stricken as she now was, and inconvenient as her narrow streets, small houses, and irregular squares had always made her, the city of Pericles kept her old charm. The magic light, which at sunrise and sunset illuminated the rose-coloured sides of the Pentelicus, would alone have made her worthy of adoration; and the birthplace of Phidias still possessed nearly all his wonderful creations. The monuments of the Acropolis were undisturbed; no profane hand had touched the pure glory of the Parthenon; the Poecile still held her brilliantly coloured decorations, fresh as the day they were completed, and the five doors of the Propylea were yet open to the blue sky.

Antony was not artistic by nature, and his career as a soldier had, naturally, not developed any love of art; yet he was not insensible to the charm of beautiful things. Rome had many rich sculptures, and he had grown up among them; and the Greek education which, in common with most Patrician youths, he had received had made him familiar with the works of Homer and the wisdom of Plato. He therefore approached the bridge of Ilisos in a spirit of reverence.

Athens was not only a venerated sanctuary with the glory of four centuries behind her, who had given the world a radiance of wisdom and culture which had never been equalled; she was still a centre of life and prosperity. Her colleges, though fewer and not so richly endowed as the schools of Alexandria, kept their ancient standards of excellence. Although not the equals of those of the old days, philosophers, poets, and artists still gathered there, together with fencers, horsemen, athletes, disk and javelin throwers; all youths who were faithful to the tradition of keeping a sound mind in a healthy body. Educated in the ideals of that republican past which had made their country great, these young men were full of fire and enthusiasm. A generous instinct gave them a natural sympathy for high aims, for all that recalled the heroes of their native land. On hearing of the death of Cato, they covered their heads with ashes; at the call of Brutus the élite of the country had perished at Philippi; and to-day Mark Antony, as opposed to Octavius, represented to them the old liberal spirit of Rome.

The Triumvir was careful not to check this flattering popularity. Knowing how these sons of Themistocles respected military pomp, he entered Athens on horseback, clad in cuirass and helmet, with clashing arms; then, in accordance with the simplicity of the civilian customs, he partook of the unpretentious hospitality that was offered him in the ancient palace of the Archons. His customary gold plate, silken togas, and couches were banished; he had a frugal meal prepared and, recalling the example set by Cæsar, he put on a woollen cloak and, preceded by a solitary lictor, went on foot up the hill of the Acropolis.

During his stay at Athens he never deviated from this simple manner of living; whether his unlimited power had wrought a sudden change in his views, or breathing the air of Greece had made him feel the beauty of moderation, his attitude astonished all those who had known him. His conduct was that of a real chief, and the sentences that he was called upon to pronounce all bore the stamp of balanced judgment. Not content with merely edifying the Athenians, it was soon apparent that he wished to win them. It was the season for the festival of Adonis. He consented to celebrate this with them and ingenuously joined in the rite of the quickly blooming, quickly fading flowers which symbolized the premature death of the son of Myrrha. He graciously listened to the elegies recited by the mourning women, who wept for the young god; and to the hymns with which these same women, now crowned with roses, filled the air the following day, in token of his resurrection. He presided over the different competitions held on the Pnyx, and, surrounded by a group of distinguished Athenians, awarded prizes to those who had won distinction in either athletics or oratory.

Had Antony become a convert to the virtuous life? Could such a sudden transformation be genuine? Was the former worshipper of Venus given over to gaining the affections of the masses? Some people who were interested in his future greatness believed this and rejoiced in it. But the real reason for this abrupt change lay in his craving for new sensations. Did he want to amuse? Did he hope to mystify? Not exactly; but the blood which bubbled in his veins was too strong and active to be satisfied with living one life only. By playing many parts this sturdy actor sought the illusion of crowding more into his life.

But his real character quickly came out. He suddenly grew weary of these simple pleasures and dull duties. The shores of Asia with its gracious fields were within easy reach, and its cities offered every luxury and entertainment. So one fine morning he shook the sacred dust of the Acropolis from his buskins, and taking ship, set sail for Antioch.

This metropolis, at that time the third in importance in the world, seemed, at a distance, to hang from the sides of the Coryphean mountains. Long before entering the harbour of Seleucia, voyagers were astonished to see the gigantic military forts which scaled the rocky slopes and crowned the summit with their crenelated walls. The city itself was on the banks of the Orontes, a white mass gleaming through the cypress trees. In addition to the theatres, gymnasiums, aqueducts, circuses, and racecourses, common to all large capitals, that of Syria had a Corso, a wide avenue, bordered from one end to the other by quadruple lines of columns. This splendid boulevard was a rendezvous for the world of fashion, and a constant stream of people passed up and down it day and night; on certain days the life and animation surpassed even that of the Roman Forum. The innumerable attractions of Antioch, especially since the decline of Athens, had brought many people to settle there, and it had, as well, a large floating population: Persians, Jews, Orientals of every country, to say nothing of the courtesans who flocked there from Susa, Ecbatana, often from the banks of the Ganges. Under the influence of these transient dwellers and of its tremendous commercial power, equalled only by that of Alexandria, manners and morals had gradually become corrupt. It was declared to be the most depraved city between Paphlagonia and Palmyra, a region noted for its scandalous living. As an example of the loose customs of the day, when the feast of Maia was celebrated, groups of naked girls ran through the streets, waving torches, while others, in like state, swam in the clear waters of the fishing pools, in full sight of the crowds.

This corrupt atmosphere had an immediate effect upon Mark Antony. The instant he breathed it his spirits rose; he was exhilarated, cheerful, full of his old keen desire for the pleasure of living. But did not everything in the palace of the Seleucides—a restoration of the one which had made Sardanapalus famous—tend to increase this feeling? As he strolled along the Corso, watching the beautiful and fascinating women file past, their look seemed to say: "Every hour cheated of its joy is empty as the grave!" How far he was from those austere assemblies of the Pnyx, or the house of the Archons! With impetuous vehemence, he stripped off his disguise of Athenian simplicity and was once more his natural self. The grave demeanour and governmental cares with which he had been occupied since the Macedonian days were succeeded by a period of license proportionate to his tedious term of self-restraint. No longer influenced by any fear of criticism, as everyone about him was of the same mind, yielding to the flattering libertines who surrounded him he put aside all dignity and, oblivious of his rank, joined in their orgies of debauchery. Every evening a group of perfumed courtesans, brought in by Anaxanor, the flute-player, swayed in rhythmic movement on the rich carpets, displaying the grace of their bodies, accompanied by languorous melodies upon the flute. The dancer, Xantos, directed the performances of the mimes and buffoons, and Medrador, whose father had grown rich by means of the wine-cellars of King Tissaphernus, had charge of the table which, in extravagant abundance and delicacy, had never been surpassed, even in the most famous Asiatic courts.

Such an establishment necessarily entailed great expense. How could the money for this be supplied save by the usual methods of the conqueror in a vanquished country—an increase of taxation? Antony did not fail to follow the example of his predecessors. He claimed that, as Brutus and Cassius had drawn heavily upon the resources of these provinces, he was entitled to get even more. Certain towns that had already been severely taxed were called upon for new contributions. "That will teach them the folly of upholding a bad cause," said Antony, with his genial smile.

These hardships, however, were not accepted everywhere with equal submission. Hybreas, the champion of Cappadocia, made bold to say, when the master appeared: "If Mark Antony demands a double, a triple tribute from us, will he provide a double, a triple crop each year?"

So far from annoying him, this remark pleased the Triumvir, for he had a sense of humour, and appreciated it in others, even though the joke was at his own expense. He replied with a jest and let the province of Cappadocia go free of extra taxes.

The good faith which he usually showed in his dealings gained him indulgence, and his generosity was an antidote to his plundering. He often restored with one hand what he had taken with the other. The day before he left Antioch, wishing to reward the chef who had prepared the feasts which he and his friends had enjoyed, he gave him a palace which had served as a ransom for a wealthy citizen of Magnesia.

His stay at Ephesus brought about the undoing of Mark Antony. Though not less dissolute than Antioch, this celebrated city was in a way different. Entirely under the influence of the priests, since the temple of Diana had been erected with its marble columns, it had impressed on everything, even the most objectionable, the stamp of her worship. Magnificent festivals attracted not only pilgrims, but hordes of suspicious characters, to whom the sanctuary afforded a safe refuge. All this mass of men, this mixture of charlatans, mountebanks, magicians, jugglers, and sorcerers, skilful in exploiting vice as well as superstition, helped to transform these fêtes into wild revels. And these horrors, these infamous liberties, took place at the shrine of Diana and under the guise of her worship. In leaving Delos and approaching the Syrian coast, where all things became tainted and corrupt, the character of the chaste goddess was changed. She who on the other side of the water breathed forth strength and modesty had become a coarse idol of the flesh. It seemed as though in changing her dwelling-place the very essence of her being was altered; the divine huntress had abandoned her bow and arrow, and the decadent imagination of some unknown sculptor had coarsened and distorted the lines of her virginal body. Oh, nymph of the woods, in what profane regions have your flying feet strayed!

When the Ephesians heard that the Triumvir was on his way to visit their city they determined, with their passion for deifying everything, to welcome him as they would Dionysos. Chariots preceded him, filled with girls representing Bacchantes; a group of Pans and Satyrs surrounded him, dancing to the accompaniment of the flute. They saluted him with the names given to the god himself, greeting him with the verses sacred to his worship: "Hail to thee, Heracles, giver of all joys! Oh, Bacchus, to whom we owe the juicy fruit of the vines! Omestes, sweet as tender figs, thou art welcome!" The whole town, wherever Antony's chariot passed, was decorated with ivy and garlands of flowers. Music resounded and blue clouds of incense mounted heavenward.

If Antony did not actually believe himself to be the son of Jupiter, he was drunk with flattery and claimed some of the privileges of divine ancestry, chiefly that of being beyond the control of human laws. His caprices were limitless. He attired himself in silk and cloth of gold, had a chorus of dancers in continual attendance, and held his court with Olympian bearing.

But with all this he did not, for a moment, forget the selfish object of his journey. He was willing to be adored, but not to make the least sacrifice. The Ionians had put up a strong protest, but he did not lessen by a farthing the tax of two hundred thousand talents which he had levied upon them. All that they gained was an extension of the time of payment, and that only because the request came to him through the beautiful Corelia, who was, for the time being, in high favour.

Antony soon tired of travelling from one city to another and decided that it was more in keeping with his dignity to summon the kings, his vassals, to him, than to go to them. He chose Tarsus for his residence and announced that henceforth the sovereigns should seek him, and he made it quite clear that the continuance of their sovereignty depended on his pleasure.

None dared disobey his orders. Along the dusty roads, under the placid skies, cavalcades and litters, chariots drawn by oxen, by elephants with majestic tread, moved steadily on, followed by a long file of dromedaries, bearing the baggage with oriental pomp. As the caravans drew near lances flashed, armour gleamed, the standards bore curious devices, the swarm of men and beasts presented a motley appearance. On arriving at the city gates a herald went forward and, through a silver trumpet, announced the name of the august visitor. The kings of Antioch and Sysima, the satrap, Palemon, Herod, who reigned in Judea, and Adallas of Sidonia, were all duly announced, also the tetrarchs of Lycaonia and Pontus, the governor of Commagene, as well as the rulers of Thrace and Arabia.

Tanned by the hot sun of the East, many of them seemed sad and very weary. One and all they hated this conqueror, but as soon as they were in his presence they were animated by the hope of some reward to be obtained, some honour or promotion to be secured.

Luxuriously installed in a tent, which served as a tribunal, Antony received the various suppliants with great ceremony and dealt out his favours. The report got abroad that the personal attractiveness of the claimant influenced his decisions, and the princesses hastened to seek an audience. He received a visit from the noted beauty, Glaphyra, and her gracious charms secured the throne of Phrygia for her son; the young widow of Aristobulus was assured of the permanence of her crown; Herod's devoted wife, Mariamne, in spite of her reserve, succeeded in winning what she desired for her husband.

But the one whom, above all others, he desired and expected, the Queen of Egypt, had not come. Why was she so late? The command had been sent to her as to the others; perhaps the wish to see *her* had inspired the general edict. Cleopatra's failure to appear was all the more remarkable as she had certain affairs to settle with him. As an ally of

Rome, her attitude during the late war had given grounds for criticism. When the avengers of Cæsar had asked the aid of her fleet she had urged the pretext of a tempest which prevented her from sending it. But this prudence could be interpreted as a desire to keep on good terms with both parties. So she had much to explain and should lose no time. Antony had written to her several times. The first letters had been official notes from a ruler to a queen, desiring her presence according to the prescribed form then in use. Her replies had been vague. He then wrote more urgently. Getting no satisfactory result from his efforts, his anger was aroused. Was this daughter of the Lagidæ trifling with him? Had she forgotten that her father owed the restoration of his throne to the gracious power of Rome? And her own position? To-morrow, if he so decreed . . .

One day he decided to send her a letter of command. But what could he say? After all he was only a man, tormented by his passions, who, unaccustomed to any resistance, felt his desire turning to exasperation. Like Jupiter with his thunderbolts, he imagined that the elements would obey him and that this coveted woman would come submissively if he frightened her sufficiently. When he found that his commands were disregarded, just as his advances had been ignored, he tried to forget her. He was rich in resources and had many mistresses. One succeeded the other with incredible speed, as though a constant change could give to each the power to efface the memory of Cleopatra. Each time that he clasped a new love to his breast he would, for the moment, feel free from the desire for her presence, would think that he had effectually rid himself of the craving for her. But these periods of oblivion passed quickly and the longing for the absent one returned, stronger than ever. Although there had never been any definite bond between them, he unconsciously nourished toward Cleopatra the kind of rancour that he would have felt toward a mistress who had betrayed and deserted him. He was beginning to hate her; and yet, he still longed for her coming.

Tarsus, like Antioch and Ephesus, was one of the principal cities of Asia Minor. Situated almost at the mouth of the Cydnus, that ice-cold river which, to the young Alexander, had felt like the first touch of death—it had the animated life of a port, while the neighbouring forests of myrtles lent it the glamour of romance. The temple of Apollo made it a shrine for men of letters, and it showed a tendency toward idealism which prepared the way for that apostle who was soon to be born there, and who was destined to preach the gospel of Christ within its walls. In the meantime it was the sanctuary of Aphrodite, and innumerable voluptuous statues, always laden with abundant offerings, bore witness to the fervent worship of this goddess. Thus associated with divinity and screened by the range of the Taurus mountains, watered by bubbling springs and swept by fragrant breezes, Tarsus was an ideal resting-place.

If satisfied ambition could content the human heart, Antony should have been perfectly happy, for each day brought him new homage and more complete submission. In his innermost being, however, uneasiness and discontent reigned. He was not altogether sensual and was, at times, overcome by a noble sadness. He craved an object for his ambition, an aim for the exuberance which carried him away. On the days when this discontent tormented him beyond endurance he sought a counter-irritant, not in commonplace pleasures—they no longer amused him—but in healthy physical exercise, which, while it lasted, drove away all irritating thought. He would fling himself on one of his Syrian steeds, under whose delicate skin the veins were clearly visible, whose nostrils seemed to breathe fire, and with bridle-rein hanging loose would ride headlong through torrents and down valleys. This exhilarating exercise restored at once that vitality and enthusiasm which his temporary depression had apparently crushed for ever. He seemed born again, full of fierce energy and joyousness, as though he had just gained a new victory, more glorious than any he had yet won.

These rides often took Antony to the Ægean shore. Perhaps unconsciously he felt the need of looking out upon the sea, of questioning its depths. It was full of peace and beauty, covered with the shining gold of the setting sun. Its rippling bosom seemed to breathe. Gazing steadily at it, hearing its murmur on the beach, feeling its soft breath, it became at last a living creature to him, the woman of his dreams. In his imagination he saw two women, each aiding the other against him, both seductive, both perfidious, each having the same sovereign power to make him the happiest of men, yet taking pleasure in leaving him on this shore, solitary and forlorn.

But the days went by and although he scanned the horizon to its uttermost limits, although the winds were favourable and the sea was covered with ships, he could never see that world-renowned galley with its purple sails, which travellers returning from Alexandria had so often described to him. At last his patience gave out. He was tired of hoping against hope; all his powers availed him nothing against that far-away indifference, whose cause baffled him. Impelled by that mysterious force which controls human destinies, he finally despatched an ambassador with orders to use all possible persuasions to induce Cleopatra to come to him.

IV

Cleopatra

DAY was just breaking. Within its inlaid walls the bed-chamber was cool and shadowy. The rose-covered trellis outside the windows made a soft, dim light. At the farther end stood an ivory bed, its four feet fashioned like a leopard's paws. Cleopatra lay quiet on her pillow, her arms above her head, her eyes closed, but she was not sleeping. Still drowsy, she followed, waking, the happy dreams that had come to her in sleep. Ever since that first letter from Antony when, with her unfailing feminine instinct, she had read between the lines an appeal that was more than a request from the Triumvir of Rome to a subject, her thoughts had been full of him. He had not forgotten her, then! This mighty adventurer, this conqueror who was welcomed everywhere as a god, was willing to pay any price for the privilege of seeing her again. Not only was her pride flattered by this homage, but she felt that her position as a sovereign, which had been disturbed by continued tumults and uprisings, would be strengthened.

It must be remembered that Cleopatra was still in the restlessness of youth and her blood had all the heat of the tropics. Ardent passions bring profound depressions in their train. How could she suppress this tempest within her? She hungered after tender embraces, the warmth of declared love; the fierce delight of that passion which wounds and transports at the same time—and she had only her present empty existence, with its succession of lonely days, in which life seemed to slip away, vanishing drop by drop, like water falling from a fountain. If she had followed the natural impulse of her impetuous nature she would have accepted eagerly Antony's first invitation. Reflection, however, counselled her to wait. The more her coming was desired, the greater would be the stimulus of a delay. This scheme was well devised, but it nearly brought fatal disaster by arousing Antony's anger and his desire to show his authority, and submission was the last virtue of which Cleopatra was capable. The mere suggestion of restraint woke all her instinct of rebellion. This conqueror of the Orient should not imagine that because he had made vassals of a set of corrupt princes, he could compel her to appear before his tribunal, subdued and trembling. She would never come into his presence in that manner.

A step on the carpet interrupted her reveries. It was Charmian, her lady-in-waiting, her confidante and friend, who was privileged to approach the Queen at any time. She had been associated with Cleopatra from the latter's early childhood, when Ptolemy Auletes had chosen her from all the nobility of Athens, that his adored daughter might have always near her an agreeable and cultured companion: one who would speak to her in the language of the gods. Charmian, in addition, had the task of teaching the young princess the art of walking with ease, of dressing in taste, and of draping her form with those graceful linen folds which the women of Tanagra have immortalized. The pupil soon surpassed her instructor, but the changed relations in no way lessened their friendship. It resulted on the one side in a deep admiration and blind devotion lasting until death, and on the other, in a confidence without reserve.

If Charmian came earlier than usual this morning and seemed hurried, it was because she had important news. At dawn a Roman galley had entered the port, bringing Quintus Dellius, the ambassador of Mark Antony.

Cleopatra was much stirred by this announcement. If Antony had sent an ambassador it was because he had something in mind which letters were inadequate to explain. What could this be? Perhaps only a reiteration of his former invitation. But in what form would it come? Reproaches were inevitable. Her apparent indifference to his requests had merited them. The idea, however, brought a smile to her scornful lips. She knew how to manage her excuses. But there might be another explanation of this messenger, and the thought made her uneasy. What if the ambassador were a Roman magistrate? What if he brought papers giving him the power to question her and demand a reckoning? As a subject of Rome she must be cautious. How could she explain her failure to send assistance during the recent war, and that in the face of repeated and urgent demands?

But Charmian assured her that it was useless to torment herself with these questions. Let her go to Antony, as she had gone to Cæsar, and all would be well. Did she not possess the divine gift of fascination which stole men's reason and made them see everything through her eyes?

In her heart Cleopatra was of the same opinion, especially in regard to Antony. She understood how strongly he was influenced by the magnetism of a beautiful woman. But who was his messenger and what course should she take with him? For a moment she was perplexed, but only for a moment. She decided to treat this messenger in the same manner that she would have treated Antony, had he come in person. The first thing to do was to make herself beautiful, very beautiful; to select the apparel which would show her charms to the greatest advantage and make her irresistible. The other matters would adjust themselves in the course of conversation.

She rapped three times upon a brass plaque to summon her attendants. The blinds were raised and the fresh morning light poured into the room, while the servants, like a swarm of bees, set about their daily tasks. Cleopatra arose from her bed and passed on to the pool where a warm bath had been prepared. She went down the six steps into the marble basin, which was just deep enough for the water to cover her as she lay in its gentle embrace. A Nubian slave was always in readiness to give her a vigorous rubbing when she came out of her bath. This massage made her transparent skin glow, and then she was again rubbed softly with nard brought from Sidon. Other women came in their turn to contribute to the care of her precious body. One blanched her dainty hands with a lotion made of hyssop; another polished her rosy nails; still another, squatting on her heels, touched with carmine the extremities of her tiny feet, then put on the soft-lined sandals.

The hair-dresser stood in especially high favour. Her profession enjoyed various privileges, not the least being her right to have long and intimate audiences with the Queen, to be consulted, and, above all, to be allowed to place a flower, a feather, or the diadem, in the Queen's hair, thus having her chance to win royal approval. Iras, the Persian, had filled this office for the past three years. The fairy-lightness of her touch and her sweet breath were celebrated. Hearing them spoken of when the young girl was an attendant of Mariamne, Herod's wife, whose auburn hair reached to her knees, Cleopatra had elected to have her for her own service. This served the double purpose of securing a talented artist for herself, and of depriving a woman whom she detested of a cherished attendant.

Iras had been brought to the Egyptian court by a merchant of perfumes, who, under pretext of giving her a new essence to inhale, had put her to sleep and carried her off without resistance. Although the new court was far grander than that of Judea, even as the sun surpasses the moon, Iras wept floods of tears at the change. Her companions, who envied her good fortune, exclaimed: "What, you weep, when your hands have the distinguished honour of adorning the divine Cleopatra!" But Iras had a loving heart and the splendour of her new surroundings could not reconcile her to the separation from Queen Mariamne, to whom she was warmly attached. This, at least, was her feeling for the first few days when, still a novice, she assisted at the ceremony of the royal toilet.

One day, Cleopatra, noticing the pallor of her serving-woman, spoke to her. In her incomparably musical voice she inquired why the young girl was so sad. "Are you homesick? Is it regret at leaving your family, or your lover?" Iras replied that her mother was dead and that she had left no lover behind on the shores of the Aracus. She could not, however, cease to grieve for Jerusalem and Herod's palace, where the Queen had been so unfailingly kind to her.

However insignificant the feelings of a slave might be in the eyes of this world-famous beauty, Cleopatra was touched by the ardent sincerity of Iras. It was just at the time when she had returned from Rome, alone and full of grief. She had a sudden wish to make this young girl, who was practically in exile, grow fond of her. Nothing could be easier. A few kind words, some presents offered with tact, quickly warmed the poor little heart that distress had chilled. Giving her her freedom later completed the conquest and aroused in Iras as fervent an adoration as any divinity had ever been offered; a flame willing to consume itself at any moment for the Queen, and ready, too, to burn itself out the day that this adored mistress ceased to illuminate the world.

"Quick, Iras," Cleopatra said that morning, when

she wished to be especially beautiful. "Take off my fillet and try to surpass yourself." She sat down before her dressing-table, which was covered with combs of different sizes, iridescent glass bottles, tiny jars filled with unguents, dainty puffs in boxes of powdered orris-root and other cosmetics; gold turtles, whose pierced shells held long hairpins. Cleopatra bent her head, and while the negro women, immobile as bronze statues, held a silver mirror that she might see her reflection, Iras passed a comb of amber tortoise-shell through the Queen's hair.

No one was more skilful than the young Persian girl in handling the Queen's flowing tresses. It was like play for her to spread them out, then turn and twist them, lift them up and arrange them in a different fashion each day. These changes of coiffure made an inexhaustible subject of conversation between the Queen and her attendant. They discussed them, pronounced them more or less becoming, tried new ornaments fit for varying occasions. Which was most suitable for to-day? There was no time to lose in experiments. They must decide without delay how Cleopatra would receive the messenger from Mark Antony. After a moment's thought she decided against the crown, the ancestral head-dress, the diadem; they were all too pretentious, too formal. It was as a woman, a beautiful woman, that she would appear before this ambassador. She chose the Athenian style: a simple cord attached by a ribbon above the nape of her neck, and, confining the thick waves of her hair, three bands outlined her delicate head.

Iras was no less expert in the use of rouge and perfumes. In Phœnicia she had become familiar with salves and ointments compounded from roses and lilies and the blossoms of the privet. Prepared by her these unguents had a marvellous effect in making limbs supple, and she alone knew how to make flesh shine like polished marble by rubbing it with a powder made of crushed mother-of-pearl. Cleopatra never allowed any one but her dear Iras to put the roses in her cheeks, to accentuate the arch of her splendid eyebrows, and to darken the natural shadows under her eyes by the skilful use of a swan's feather touched with sibium.

When Cleopatra was thus shod, coifed, and redolent from head to foot with sweet perfumes, the ladies in charge of the robes came in. They brought in great chests in which the robes lay without a crease to spoil their freshness. Raising the covers they laid out two, three, four, until the Queen had made her choice. She chose a saffron-coloured silk tunic, embroidered with narcissus blossoms. Fastened to her shoulders by two amber clasps the tunic left her arms and bosom bare. Above this a transparent drapery hung, woven by the women of Cos and made, so the legend went, of the condensed vapours of the morning mists of springtime, the tissue that is known to-day as "the Virgin's threads."

Cleopatra urged her attendants to make haste. She was impatient at their delay in fastening a fold, or arranging her girdle, those innumerable details of her toilet which usually entertained her. She was anxious to be ready, eager to meet this unknown man with whom she was planning such an exciting battle. When her string of pearls had been clasped around her neck, her arms and fingers adorned with bracelets and rings, she gave a final glance at her exquisite reflection in the mirrors and left the room.

Mark Antony had chosen for his ambassador Quintus Dellius, famous in the Odes of Horace, one of the most charming and well informed men of his day. A wit, a learned historian, as well as a poet from time to time, he had the adaptable disposition which real intelligence gives, and though quick at epigrams he could be, when it was to his advantage, considerate and gracious. The consistent policy which he had successfully followed through life had been to make friends with the man in command, to devote himself exclusively to forwarding his patron's interests, and invariably to quit his service on the instant that his star set, and to attach himself to the next one in power. Thus before the battle of Philippi he had been the friend of Cassius, after the battle of Actium he became the inseparable companion of Octavius. At present he thought that all the odds were in favour of Antony, and, deciding that the latter was likely to hold his own, his devotion to him was unmistakable. No one could have been better qualified for the delicate mission which led him to Alexandria than this practised go-between, who thoroughly understood the ways of women.

As the Queen, surrounded by her guard, mounted the throne, which stood before a tapestry of birds and flowers, the guest was summoned. He was a Roman, short of stature, with refined features, an alert, gracious expression, whose distinguished bearing marked him as an Aristocrat. He saluted her at the threshold with sword-point lowered and his left hand touching his shoulder. Instead of coming forward at once he remained motionless for a moment looking steadily at Cleopatra as though his amazement at her beauty had taken away his senses. Then he spoke:

"Before all else, O mighty Queen, my master, Mark Antony, whose mouthpiece I am, salutes you; he wishes you glory, happiness, and lasting prosperity."

"You will take him my good wishes in return," she replied, smiling; and added: "But his hopes have already been fulfilled in his victories."

The ambassador replied: "You are mistaken, O divine sovereign; Mark Antony's happiness will never be complete, he will never feel that he is truly great, until you honour him with your gracious presence."

This was surely an auspicious beginning; but how could Cleopatra be certain that these were not merely preliminary formulas. She must find out whether this envoy had not some other communication to make, some personal message which would indicate the real discontent of Mark Antony.

At her command the attendants withdrew, and their departure seemed to lighten the atmosphere, free it from all suggestion of restraint. The two now felt at ease, each eager to be agreeable to the other.

"Why have you come to see me?" asked the Queen in a tone of playful frankness, as though inviting his confidence. "Tell me all; keep nothing back. I must know the real reason for the Triumvir's desiring my presence; what intentions has he in regard to me?" and the expression of her eyes seemed to add: "If you do as I ask, if you speak sincerely, you shall have no cause to regret it."

When she had been assured that Antony had despatched his ambassador only because of his impatience to see her and renew their former friendly relations, her anxiety vanished. She had the sensation of breathing more freely, as though a window had been opened. Her calculations had not betrayed her. In deferring her visit to Antony she had whetted his desire to see her. But would he not make her pay for her coquetry? Was he not, perhaps, planning some revenge?

She made various excuses for her delay, which in no way deceived Dellius. He was still more skeptical when, under pretence of timidity, she said that she had put off her departure on account of current reports concerning the reception accorded to certain princesses on their arrival at Tarsus.

Judging it wise to reassure her he protested: "What! Glaphyra! Eutrope! Beggars already dethroned, or fearing to be! Vassals who threw themselves at the conqueror's feet with the most doubtful intentions! What comparison can there be between them and your gracious self?" Then, adopting the tone of a priest addressing an idol, he went on:

"O thou, the well-beloved of Osiris! August sovereign whose sceptre covers land and sea! Woman above all other women! Understand that your presence is expected with reverence as well as eagerness. From the moment that you set foot on Roman territory, gracious deeds will follow you and the whole people will pay you homage."

But this was not what interested Cleopatra. One word as to Antony's personal sentiments would have given her more satisfaction. How could she learn what these were? How was she to find out whether he was summoning her as a sovereign, with whom he wished to renew an alliance, or as a vassal who was already in his debt? Or simply because in his heart of hearts old memories of her still lingered?

As he watched her and talked with her, Dellius began to understand what an exceptional creature she was and why his master thought her worth the price he was paying. It was not alone her beauty which made her so wonderful. In gazing at her a vague uneasiness, an indefinable fear took possession of him. If her animation sometimes caused an uncontrollable tremor, her sensuous languor, at others, gave promise of untold delights. His keen insight told him the influence such a woman would have in the life of Antony, who was now nearly forty years old, that dangerous age in sensual natures. The gallant adventures of his youth no longer sufficed; he was now experiencing an actual sentimental hunger which comes to men who, without genuine passion, have lived a life of excess. An overwhelming love at this time would be his salvation. He would give himself up to it without reservation, and however unworthy the woman who inspired it might be, she would not fail to acquire a power whose limit it was impossible to foresee.

Dellius felt that Cleopatra would be this ruler over Antony's destiny; so he decided that he would not only carry out his master's mission and persuade her to go to Tarsus, but that he would also make her his patron and friend. Later, when she had become the Egeria of Antony, perhaps she would recall the service he had rendered her and would help him to attain his own end, which was a consulship.

From that moment the shrewd man set to work to interpret the sentiments of his master. He described him as deeply in love, which Antony certainly was not as yet, though he was ready to be; pretended that he was obsessed by the memory of Cleopatra; that for days at a time he did nothing but wait for her coming. He was often seen standing at the mouth of the Cydnus, beaten by the winds, watching the incoming ships. It would be inhuman to prolong his misery. One word from her would set his mind at rest. If she would only send him that word of promise Antony would be happier than if he had conquered fresh kingdoms.

"Is it possible," added Dellius, as though talking to himself, "is it possible to have been near the divine Cleopatra without experiencing on leaving her a regret which nothing but seeing her again can cure?"

An indescribable dread disturbed the Queen's mind. She felt that this was the decisive moment of her life, and a thrill went through her. She had a burning desire for the joys that the future might hold, and wanted to hurry on to them. She had the impulse to cry out: "I am going! I shall start tomorrow!" The attitude, however, which she had adopted from the beginning still held her captive. Even to the end she must play her part, seem to hesitate, to be difficult to win, and above all, let no one suspect the longing she had to be forced to go.

"Since it is necessary, since the Triumvir demands it, I will go to bear him my homage," she said.

But this did not satisfy Dellius. He had too little faith in women to trust to a vague promise made from a sense of duty. He wanted a definite statement, with no reservations. So he began to protest again. It was not as a sovereign that Antony would receive the Queen of Egypt. He longed for her coming and would welcome her with the reverence due a goddess.

Such words could not fail to win the consent which was already in her heart. Cleopatra's pride was safe, she had been sufficiently implored; so, with a smile, she promised to set out for Tarsus before the days began to shorten.

Although eager to announce the good tidings, Dellius accepted her invitation to stay a few days in Alexandria. It would not be a waste of time because, although his master's mission had been successfully accomplished, his own was not fulfilled. In bringing Cleopatra to Tarsus, where she would become the mistress of Antony, he had the secret hope that he would thereby win their double gratitude.

Each had his own end to gain and the two held long conversations, usually with Antony for the subject. Dellius made a point of dwelling on the Triumvir's various characteristics; his tastes, his qualities, for her information when opportunity offered. Undoubtedly Antony had always cared for display, but the incense which Asia had burned at his feet had so intoxicated him that he had become almost obsessed by the love of ostentation. Nothing was gorgeous enough, no banquet sufficiently resplendent, to satisfy him.

"How severe and gloomy Rome to-day would seem to him; on the other hand how enchanted he would be with the magnificence that reigns here," said Dellius.

Further persuasion was needless; Cleopatra understood. A plan was already forming in her mind. She saw in imagination the glorious vision she would present to Antony's astonished eyes.

The next day she began to make ready for the journey. Although she commanded all possible haste, for she was now really eager to go, the preparations took nearly a month. It would not have been possible to complete in less time the marvellous equipment for the voyage of this new Queen of Sheba.

The rising sun cast the soft light of one of those ideal summer days when all outlines are blurred and blend in the mysterious charm of woods and sky. Under a cluster of sycamore trees, which shaded the public square of Tarsus, Antony was holding court as Proconsul, assisted by petty rulers, magi, and prætors, and, governed by his somewhat rudimentary conscience, deciding the various cases according to the Roman law. He was besieged by a crowd, each having his own special petition, and each in turn being granted a hearing. The court was following the speech of one of the advocates in respectful silence when excited murmurs began to be heard. Men came running up from the shores of the Cydnus with strange tales. The agitation spread rapidly and Aphrodite's name was on all lips. The people had been carefully trained by the priests, and their religion had accustomed them to believe in the proximity of the gods and in their possible intervention. But this strange tale surpassed the most wonderful fables. It was reported that the daughter of Zeus was sailing up the river on a golden galley resounding with music. She had been recognized, not only by her supernatural beauty, but by those symbols with which painters and sculptors had always represented her. Reclining in an enormous shell, this goddess seemed to be rising from the sea. Purple sails adorned the galley and a troop of nereids hung in the rigging, waving fans, while tiny cupids scattered rose leaves at her feet. Every moment new messengers arrived with fresh details that surpassed all the preceding ones. The galley's sails were of silk; purple draperies covered the decks; fifty black men from Koursch rowed rhythmically, with oars tipped with silver; light smoke from the galley wafted the sweet perfume of cinnamon and of incense.

The public square was gradually deserted as curiosity overcame the people. Those who, the instant before, had been struggling for a place near the Tribunal, had suddenly vanished. The ever-growing crowd was now jostling each other on the banks of the Cydnus. Shouts and cries of admiration went up. The whole city of Tarsus was soon on the quais, and, in an ecstasy of enthusiasm, welcomed the approaching goddess and thanked Zeus for sending her.

On hearing these astounding reports Antony was as one distracted. He put his hand to his head; he struggled for breath. Beyond all doubt it was she! That goddess whom his impatient heart had so long craved! She had taken him by surprise!

As he could not permit himself to join the crowd and rush to meet her, he called Dellius.

"Go," he said, "receive Cleopatra with all honour. Put at her disposal all that she wishes, and ask her to sup with me at the palace this evening."

Antony was too much agitated to resume the interrupted hearings. Of what importance were individual interests, or even those of the Republic, in comparison with this overwhelming event? Assessors, registrars, witnesses were all dismissed, and in his ecstasy, wishing to share his joy with others, he granted all the petitions laid before him.

Dellius returned with the message that Cleopatra warmly appreciated the invitation from the Triumvir, but that this first evening she wished to have him as her guest. She would expect him on board her galley at the time appointed for supper.

Then it was really true! It was she! She had crossed the seas to come to him! In a few moments he would see her, be at the same table with her! How should he approach her; what words of greeting should he use? He was perplexed, for proper words never come in the moment of excitement. He tried to imagine the scene. His attitude would be courteous, certainly; how otherwise? But he must have a certain majesty of bearing. His title of Triumvir placed him above all other sovereigns. In the eyes of his colleagues it was important that he should maintain his prestige. Cleopatra had failed in her duty as an ally of Rome and it would be necessary to inquire the reasons. With all possible consideration, yet with firmness, he would ask: "What part did you take in the war? Why did you fail us?"

Full of these thoughts, he began his preparations. He chose his most beautiful silver breast-plate, the one by an Athenian artist representing Achilles being dipped in the Styx by his mother. He put perfume on his face, rubbed it in his hair, and, a superb martial figure, his head erect, every nerve alert, as though he were going into battle, set out on the avenue leading to the river. The plane trees cast darker shadows in the evening light. Between the trunks of the trees the setting sun was like burnished copper. When he reached the river banks the brilliant sunset light had faded, but before him shone the marvellous galley. From the tips of the masts to the water's edge it was a mass of draperies illuminated by torches. It was not possible to count them, but the shining whole was like a fire mounting almost to the sky.

That famous supper at Tarsus, that evening meeting between those two beings who were to stir the world and leave a path of fire across the centuries, is assuredly one of the enthralling moments of history. Putting aside the magnificence of the entertainment, the prodigal abundance of the feast which this daughter of the Lagidæ had planned to dazzle the most powerful of the Romans, to let him see that the luxury in which he lived was provincial compared with the customs and manners of her court, it was the force of the dramatic situation which appealed as these two approached each other. It was the climax of her long-planned design, the result of all her grace and wit, this taking possession of Antony's very soul, so to seduce and imprison him that he could find no escape from the binding circle of her charm. She brought to this plan all the skill of the experienced woman of the world and a heart as yet untouched by real passion.

In this meeting it was Antony who felt embarrassed and ill at ease. Although he was familiar with women's ways and accustomed to speaking freely with them, yet this charmer, with her seductive guile, the elaborate beauty of her costume, and her mysterious smile, which now mocked, now tempted him to kneel at her feet, daunted him.

"You!—at last!" . . . he exclaimed as he approached her, and that was all he dared say by way of reproach.

This heart-felt cry was so filled with satisfied longing, showed such real joy, that Cleopatra knew that she had won him. She began to make excuses for not having come before. She had been bound by so many obligations. Egypt was the source of so much anxiety. For the past two years the wheat crop had failed and there was growing discontent among her people. It was highly important to attend to the needs of her country. For a long time she had doubted the possibility of being able to leave.

But Antony's eyes were fixed on Cleopatra. He ignored the flimsy excuses, which would not have stood in her way had she desired to overcome them. He could only whisper:

"You are more beautiful than ever!"

"Do you think so?" she answered, and her smile was that of a simple girl.

Then, taking her guest by the hand, she led him to the stern of the vessel, which had been converted into a grove. They took their places on the two purple couches beside the table; and enjoying the rare delicacies, drinking old wines from golden cups, they talked of many things, while the stringed instruments made sweet music. Memories of other days came back to them, days when, reclining around a sumptuous table in brilliantly lighted rooms, Antony had gazed on Cleopatra, eager to declare his love, yet held back by conditions which so often restrain the natural inclinations. He was baulked again this evening, not by the presence of others, as in former days, but by their mutual relations. A definite explanation was necessary to clear away the political clouds which enveloped them.

Cleopatra took the initiative. To run the risk of being accused, of having to defend herself was contrary to all her instincts. Besides, what was the danger? However much at fault she might be she was confident of having a lenient judge. Whatever stand she might take, of attack or defence, she felt that her tiny hand had the power to conquer. She preferred to attack, however, and began an account of the indignities which, to uphold a just course, she had suffered at the hands of Cassius.

Three different times he had demanded recruits from her, and at each refusal she had been overwhelmed by a deluge of threats.

"The scoundrel!" muttered Antony.

She went on hurriedly: "But you, too, Antony, you counted on me, you expected my fleet to come to your aid and you had a right to expect it! You could never have doubted my good intentions; I was your surest ally. All my prayers were with you, you, the avenger of Cæsar!"

The atmosphere was changed. The discussion was taking an entirely different turn from what Antony had expected. He was completely disarmed. Hc who had planned to question her sternly, to obtain a justification, or at least some excuse for her attitude, found himself quietly listening to the voice of an enchantress.

"You have been annoyed with me?" she said, in a caressing tone.

"I have never been angry with you," he answered.

"Yes, you have. I know very well. It was at Lacedæmon. You were put out at having waited for me in vain."

But here, too, Cleopatra was ready with an explanation. She related how the gods, whose designs are impenetrably concealed from men, had seemed determined to thwart her plans. Her squadron had scarcely set sail when it had been scattered by a tempest. Several of the ships had been sunk. She, herself, ill and exhausted, had been saved only by a fortunate chance. She had returned to Alexandria at grave peril in a boat which was leaking. And when the squadron had been put in condition again it was too late; the allies had just won the battle of Philippi.

Presented in this light her conduct as an ally of Rome was not only above reproach but worthy of all praise; and Antony was not sparing in his commendation. He was deeply moved at the thought of the dangers she had passed through. He called her sublime, heroic. He was almost at the point of making excuses on his own account. Had he not been a fool in so obstinately expecting her arrival? But, on the other hand, had he not suffered torment all the days since Fate had separated them? Everywhere, at every moment, he had sought her, had hoped to see her appear. Without her he knew only unhappiness. He loved her, he had always loved her. To be content without her was impossible. And now that she was with him his passion was too strong for him. It was a burning fire that would never be quenched.

Cleopatra listened to all this gravely, making no comment. His words stirred her innermost being, and she was thrilled at the thought: "The master of the world belongs to me!" Undoubtedly she understood the passionate tone of this hero, shared his intoxication. She felt how sweet it would be to yield, to let herself be carried away by this overwhelming emotion. But the time had gone by when she was ready to give herself up at the first asking, as when she had yielded to the desire of Cæsar. The innocent young girl of those days had grown rich in experience. The years, the events, the stay at Rome had taught her many things. She recognized the value of her favours. Although fully determined to grant them, that she might bind Antony to her, unite their destinies in order to begin once more with him the game that she had lost the first time, she intended to choose her own hour.

The supper was over. Leaning back on her cushions she seemed the very image of sensual delight. She regarded Antony.

"I love you," he whispered.

"Hush," she said in the gentlest way, as though correcting a cherished child; "you must not say such things."

With a sudden frenzy and before she had time to draw back Antony pressed his passionate lips to hers. He would not be silent. He had already waited too long, had suffered too much from her delay. All hope of happiness seemed to have slipped away and he had been on the verge of despair. And now that she was really with him, she the adored idol of his heart, she told him not to speak, not to tell her of this love which meant life itself to him!

The young Queen stood up. The dying light of the candles and torches transformed her into a statuette of gold, one of those deities who are worshipped surrounded by a flashing circle of fire. She looked at Antony. A little dismayed by his ardour she asked herself whether, in spite of her ambition, she really could endure such a passionate lover.

"Wait," she said, "it grows late. I am very tired. Let me have this evening to rest."

But Antony did not stir. Leaning on the couch, his elbows on his knees and his chin in his hands, he stared distractedly at this exquisite creature. He could have remained there for ever, under those shining stars which, hour by hour increasing in brilliancy as the light of the torches faded, seemed to draw nearer, as though to share his happiness.

"Let us go," she murmured, "it is time to say good-night."

His longing eyes implored her: "Do not send me from you without a promise."

With her maddening smile, she replied, "To-morrow I will come to have supper with you."

"Until to-morrow, then," sighed Antony. Then, disappointed and baffled, his whole being tortured by visions of a joy which had seemed within his grasp and which for the moment had escaped him, he left the barge and went back to the shore.

For the next few days Cleopatra and Antony were inseparable. It was the beginning of that passion which was gradually to absorb their whole being and consume them like a fire.

If Antony had from that first evening completely lost his reason, Cleopatra had kept hers. Her mind was stronger than her emotions. Shrewd and clear-sighted, she looked into the future. With her mind's eye she saw the old dreams come back, her cherished plans of long ago. If Antony, as ruler of Rome, lacked the strength of Cæsar, his power was as far-reaching; and, if his character lacked the force, his mind the breadth of the other, she would have all the more chance of supremacy, all the greater opportunity of controlling the government.

She was seized with the desire to try the experiment without delay. A great bitterness, an ever-growing rancour was in her heart against her sister who had disputed her right to the throne and who had failed in the contest. Fleeing from her vengeance, this sister, Arsinoë, had taken refuge in the temple of Diana, at Ephesus, and, under the protection of the high priest, Megabyzus, had assumed the rôle of a sovereign. This insult to Cleopatra fell directly within the jurisdiction of the Triumvir. He alone could put a stop to it. She asked that the Princess be put to death, and also the minister, Serapion, who had upheld her in the rebellion and flight to Ephesus.

Such severities were not at all to Antony's taste. The happy hours spent at Ephesus were still fresh in his memory. Should he forfeit those for a woman's caprice? Should he thus discredit his reputation as a genial Proconsul? Besides, in violating the religious privileges he would incur the risk of making many enemies. He tried to argue, not in favour of the guilty ones, but to save his own standing. How would it look if, having shown mercy to the vanquished of his own country, he should prove pitiless to people who were subjects of Rome, and against whom he had no just complaint?

The plea had no effect. There was something in Cleopatra's character, not so much of cruelty as of a desire for domination, which would not endure resistance. Arsinoë had attacked her authority; consequently, as long as Arsinoë lived Cleopatra would not be happy. Was not she constantly in danger of some new attempt against her crown on the part of this rebel?

Antony suggested imprisonment. But no, it was Arsinoë's head that she demanded from him. He finally succeeded in rescuing the priest Megabyzus, thanks to the intervention of the Ephesians, who threatened to put the town in a state of siege rather than allow any indignity to their revered High Priest.

This was the beginning of a succession of trivial discussions. Cleopatra always succeeded in having her own way, gradually substituting her own wishes for the authority of Antony. His will was completely dominated by her, for she held him by the magic force of love. What did she give him in exchange for her first victory? Her method of evasion had succeeded too well for her to renounce it readily. Before giving herself to Antony, her instinct, a curious compound of ambition and coquetry, told her to lead him by slow degrees to the point where a whole lifetime of delight would be needed to quench his burning thirst to possess her. Prudence whispered also that, while granting him certain privileges, it would be wise to reserve the fulfilment of his happiness until they had arrived in Alexandria. Would not this be the surest means of attracting him to that city where she needed him to stabilize her power? And as to keeping him there, was not the enchanted court of the Bruchium, the prestige of her palace, its festivals, the bed of roses where Cæsar had lingered, the place where she would have the greatest chance of playing the part of the bewitching sorceress, from whose spell he would never escape?

V

The Inimitables

WHEN Antony and Cleopatra separated they planned to be together again for the winter. Antony applied himself to his affairs in Asia Minor with an unexpected industry. From early morning until late in the evening he was busy, often receiving delegates and signing papers after his supper had been served. At this rate he quickly settled the disputes between Herod and the adjoining rulers concerning frontiers, assigned to each legion the territory belonging to it, chose the governors, and, in a word, put everything in such order that he could absent himself with safety. He decided to set sail the latter part of November. The heavens were ominously dark, the sea was gray and rough, but what matter? The wind blew from the north and would drive him straight to Alexandria.

In Alexandria the presence of the Triumvir was expected with varied feelings. Those who had faith in Egypt's power and her ability for self-government deplored the arrival of the Roman ruler. To them he meant merely a new lover for the Queen, a master less gracious and perhaps more covetous than Cæsar. Others, recalling the promise of the god, regarded the hero of Philippi as a possible ally, who would restore the ancient grandeur of the kingdom. When it was announced that Antony would disembark unpretentiously, unescorted by either troops or squadron, simply as a nobleman returning the visit of a great lady, these dissensions ceased. All agreed that, as this was merely a visit of courtesy, it was necessary to welcome him warmly. Besides, the Queen's orders were explicit. She had not forgotten the lessons that Dellius had taught her. The insignificant specimen of splendour that she had displayed at Tarsus had been so much appreciated that she wanted now to show the whole wealth of her resources. She had made up her mind that Antony's reception here should entirely efface the memory of those accorded him at Ephesus and at Tarsus. She spent gold lavishly and offered prizes to those who should invent some new decoration, some spectacle which would be sure to win universal admiration.

However brilliantly decked with flags the fort, with its banners blazing from one end to the other like bonfires, however magnificent the pageants, and numerous the gateways, carpets, triumphal arches, which lined the streets where the procession passed, they made little impression on Antony; or rather, these external trappings seemed but the natural setting for his own happiness. Even the shouts of welcome were but echoes of his own exaltation. One thought alone absorbed his mind. In a moment now he would see her, would hold her in his arms. Her image obliterated everything else. His desire to possess her was the rhythm to which the whole world moved.

Four galloping horses were speeding him along the Royal Way. The pink façade of the Bruchium rose above its terraces. He was getting nearer, nearer; in another instant he would be face to face with Cleopatra.

"Will she be mine at last?" he asked himself, breathlessly. She had sworn it and it was on this understanding that they had parted. But with women, with this woman especially, with her subtle, sinuous ways, one could never tell. The uncertainty made his heart beat fast. The horses galloped steadily on, made the last slope, and Antony was at the door of the palace.

Above, on the first step, surrounded by white-mitred priests swinging censers, and by officers in rich array, Cleopatra was awaiting him. She evidently wished to remind him of the days at Tarsus, for she was draped in a sea-green robe which made her look like a nereid. Necklaces of pale green chalcedony fell over her bosom like ocean spray, and on the turquoise clasp of her belt mysterious symbols were engraved.

As Antony approached she cast a laurel branch toward him and came down to greet him. On bended knees, with outstretched arms, he saluted her with a gesture of adoration. They grasped each other's hands and spoke for a moment in low tones. Then they went up the steps of the grand stairway together in silence. They were smiling, and their expression was that of perfect, exquisite understanding.

From that day serene happiness encompassed them. The calculations, the coquetry, vanished.

There was no further anxiety save that which comes to those accustomed to a life of pleasure, when they ask themselves: "Will it last, shall I still be happy to-morrow?" This was real, absolute, supreme love. Many people, resenting the glamour of romance, have not seen, have not wished to see in this famous adventure anything but a selfish scheme, and in Cleopatra an ambitious courtesan. It is true that the persecutions of her youth had caused her to look on love as a means, had made her regard Cæsar as a protector from whom she could expect, primarily, the restoration of her kingdom, and later, if death had not come so suddenly, the crown of an empress. But with Antony it was different. At the outset, perhaps, in her dreary solitude she had certain plans in mind by which she could use him to carry out her ambitious schemes. Bereft of the great ruler by whose power she had built up her fortune, she probably dreamed of replacing him with Antony and continuing with him those bonds that the fatal poignard of Brutus had severed. But she had not reckoned on the hot blood of youth. If that voyage to Tarsus had been a snare Cleopatra was caught in her own trap. She had set out as a conqueror, sure of enforcing her will, and she had found love awaiting her to lead her captive. However attractive Antony's possessions might be, his personal charm outweighed them all. He had in a rare degree those gifts which win affection, and, in spite of all her premeditated schemes and plots, in spite of the endless intrigues which may have been combined with her feeling for him, Cleopatra undoubtedly gave him her whole heart. What is more convincing than the final tragedy? When a love affair ends with the voluntary death of the lovers, when they both kill themselves rather than live on alone, any preceding faults or failings are of small account. That last hour is the only one to be marked on the dial of history.

But at this time there was no thought of death. Day followed day, wholly given over to the joy of living. Every moment spent together created new dreams to be carried out; each desire gratified gave birth to a new desire. They seemed to have within them an inexhaustible spring from which they drank without ever quenching their thirst. The only perfect love is that where flesh and spirit are satisfied in turn, where heart and soul share in the ecstasy. To Cleopatra, who had never loved before, this feeling was a new experience. To Antony it was a surprise which plunged him in unspeakable delight. After his life of excess it would have seemed impossible for him to be thrilled by this new joy. But all other experiences were wiped out, and in this love he was born again. Like to the fire which rises, impervious to corruption, his passion for Cleopatra had burned away all stains of the past.

Their mutual happiness seemed to affect all their environment. The Queen took an exquisite pleasure in pointing out the charms of the Bruchium, that incomparable museum of art and nature. She wanted to share all its wonders with her lover. Even if she picked a rose she wanted him to inhale its fragrance as though it were an ethereal fragment of herself, and its perfume were her own breath. In showing him a marble statue from the chisel of Praxiteles, the bronze Hercules that Ptolemy VII had brought from Corinth, a bas-relief covered with figures from the Iliad; in music, or some page from a Greek drama, she sought that close contact of mind and spirit which should make them one being.

But if Antony yielded at times to the refining influence of the daughter of the Lagidæ, at other moments his own virile nature had the mastery and controlled them both.

The orgies of the Bruchium are matters of history. The moderation of modern life, with its democratic views, its lesser fortunes, its law-restricted vices, gives no hint of the extravagant living of the ancients. The scale is entirely different. There is no comparison between the provincial fêtes of to-day and the saturnalian revelries of the Romans. Our hygienic repasts offer no idea of the gluttonous feasts of Balthazar. Modern monuments, modern buildings, how pitifully poor they are compared with those colossal structures that Rameses or Darius employed thirty years of their reign in completing, and which have survived them for as many centuries! What a contrast between our richest palaces and those massive retreats of ancient kings, with their stupendous ramparts, their avenues of obelisks, the forest of columns which surrounded them! The most magnificent court of Europe would seem paltry set by the side of one of any satrap or Roman proconsul.

The world in those days belonged to the privileged few who had the entire control. The lower classes were content to look on at their revels.

There were giants in those days compared with the less virile physique of modern men. The suns which shone on their joys have set. A certain sadness depresses the modern mind, inoculated with the virus of the ideal.

Antony and Cleopatra lived at a time when they could watch life roll by like a mighty torrent. The vigour of the young world boiled in their veins with no thought of sin. To be happy was the only wisdom. They were like the followers of Epicurus, whose sole aim was to enjoy to the full the passing hour. In that wonderful city, where everything seemed planned for their delight, they spent indescribable days, days in which nothing seemed too high or too low to add to their enjoyment. As fearless in planning pleasures as in carrying them out, they were truly inimitable.

Cleopatra wished to shower every possible luxury on her guest, and she commanded that the habitual magnificence of the court life be increased in every way. A story is told by Philotas, who had come from Amphissus to finish his studies at the Serapium, of having made the acquaintance of a steward of the royal kitchens. There he saw eight wild boars waiting to be roasted before a huge brazier. "Is the Queen having a banquet this evening?" he asked. He was much astonished to learn that only the usual court was to be present, not more than a dozen guests at the outside.

"What," he cried, "eight wild boars for twelve stomachs?"

"Don't you know," answered the steward, "that only at a certain stage is a roast fit to eat? Now it is not possible to know at what moment the food must be served here, for the Triumvir may dally over a game of chess, or take a sudden fancy for a gallop to Canopus. Then there is nothing to do but to put out the fires and wait. At other times he says he is famished and must be served before the regular time. So one boar, one quarter of beef, a few geese or guinea fowls are not enough; there must be an unlimited supply!"

This is one anecdote among many which shows not only the wastefulness but the happy carelessness which surrounded this great spoiled child, Antony. Everything gave way to his capricious fancy. Cleopatra lived but to please him. Leaning on the breast of her hero, she saw life only through his eyes. At times their caresses made a paradise for both; at others she was occupied in inventing some new form of amusement to divert her lover and herself.

This constant effort was a drain on her physically and mentally and led to all kinds of follies. One of these, which happened at a banquet, is famous.

The vast hall where the guests were assembled was proportioned to conceal its height. It was encircled by arcades. In each of these a great-pawed sphinx of porphyry bore the image of a woman in Egyptian head-dress. Light poured out from torches supported by brass arms, from high candelabra spread out like sheaves, from silver tripods, these latter spouting great flames.

A hundred guests stood expectantly around the table looking at the marvellous display of golden platters, cups, and bowls. They were awaiting the arrival of Antony and Cleopatra. Presently, to the sound of music, the royal couple appeared, he, superb, god-like, in his star-covered tunic, she, adjusting her floating scarf and playing with the bracelets on her arms.

At the head of the table stood a couch supported by four crouching griffins. The royal hosts reclined there, side by side, and motioned to the guests to take their places around the table. This evening the special feature was a dance, or rather, a series of emblematic figures invented by Clitias, the celebrated Sicilian comedian. A group of twenty-four dancing girls appeared, each representing an hour; some black as night, some rosy as the dawn, others, again, the colour of broad daylight, and the different shades of dusk. These, slowly or quickly, called up in turn the image of earthly joys which come with the passing day. As each Hour gave place to the succeeding one she came to kiss the feet of the Queen.

Although this charming spectacle roused great enthusiasm and so delighted Antony that it was repeated several times, Cleopatra seemed absent-minded. She was wondering what novelty she could provide for the next evening. It was essential to set before her beloved guest something which he had never before seen. A sudden light came into her eyes; again she had found it.

"I invite you to come to-morrow to a feast which will surpass all that your eyes have ever beheld!"

And as Antony, with his generous smile, said that such a thing could not be possible, she replied, briefly:

"The supper alone will cost ten million sesterces."

Antony continued incredulous. This was not the first time that his beloved one had made extravagant statements.

"Let us lay a wager," she cried.

He agreed. "If I lose what shall I give you?"

She needed no time to consider. The word came to her lips as though she had often used it:

"A kingdom."

Had the wine gone to his head? Did he regard the Roman provinces merely as stakes to gamble with? He suggested Phœnicia.

Phœnicia, on whose coast lay Tyre, Gebel, Sidon, Berytus, all manufacturing towns, with their dyes, their carpets, their valuable carved furniture made from the cedars of Lebanon; and all sorts of other rich possessions! For the moment Cleopatra did not believe her ears. She thought he was jesting. But Antony's expression was serious. She saw that the offer was made in good faith. They touched their fingertips in token of agreement.

The report of the wager soon spread. Nothing was talked of in the city but the mysterious plan for the coming night when the Bruchium would see all its former splendours surpassed. Reasonable men shrugged their shoulders. Ten million sesterces for a single repast! It was not possible! Others crowded together to discuss among themselves what new extravagance the Queen was concocting to shake the finances of the kingdom.

The next evening the same guests assembled in the vast hall of the arcades. They were alive with curiosity. What were they gathered together to witness? What spectacle could justify the enormous expense that had been announced? But on entering the hall they saw nothing out of the ordinary. There were the same brilliant illuminations, the same gorgeous display of flowers and gold plate; all the exquisite details were just the same.

With their customary ceremony the sovereigns entered. The Queen was so simply dressed that only her jewels attracted attention. Her passion for them was well known and she had continually added to the countless treasures of the Lagidæ. Wherever she went she had acquired the rarest stones. While at Rome the Etruscan workers had given their entire time to making jewellery of her own designing. Her preference had always been for pearls. She had collected them from the Persian gulf, from Ceylon, from Malaysia, and whenever a ship-owner went to India he had orders to bring back any exceptional pearls that he found there, regardless of their cost. She wore them everywhere, around her neck, about her arms, fastened in her belt, of every shape and tint.

This evening, however, she wore only two. But such pearls! Their size, their beauty of outline, were beyond all estimate. Suspended by an invisible thread of gold, they gleamed in her ears like drops of dew on the petals of a rose. The marvel was that nature had twice produced such perfect pearls, identical in form and sheen, and that twice they had been found by man, although centuries apart. The first had been sent to Olympias from Ophir, by her son Alexander, and the second had only recently been discovered near the coast of

Malay after exhaustive searching. Did they reflect her shining eyes, were they tinted with the roses on her young cheeks; or were they, as legend says, living creatures who are affected when their fate is in the balance?

The banquet went on, lavish, but a little dull, as when an expected diversion fails. Dessert was served, and still nothing had happened. There was a general air of disappointment. Antony alone was in high spirits. He looked on himself as the winner of the wager and was amusing himself by imagining the prize he could demand. His joking became flippant:

"By Bacchus, your supper is not worth the ten million sesterces that you promised," he cried, impatiently, as he leaned toward Cleopatra.

"Don't be so certain," she replied: "you have not won yet."

She called the cup-bearer, who stood always near, and signalled to him to re-fill her cup. This golden cup, a marvel of workmanship, was supposed to have belonged to Pericles. In any case it had been carved by one of the best artists of his epoch. A troop of archers adorned it, and the handle was in the form of a beautiful woman.

All eyes were fixed on Cleopatra. What was she about to do? What miracle was to happen? For astonishing things were always expected of her.

Turning toward Antony she raised the cup to her lips, and with an expression half humorous, half solemn, said:

"Look carefully. When I have drunk this, my wager will be won." At the same time she unfastened one of the pearls and let it fall to the bottom of the foaming cup, where it was quickly dissolved.

Cries of horror went up, as in the face of an irreparable disaster.

Having emptied the cup, Cleopatra made ready for a second sacrifice.

Antony seized her wrist.

"Spare your jewels," he cried; "I acknowledge my defeat."

The Queen hesitated; and he added, "Phœnicia is yours!"

What was the use of doubling the sacrifice? It was said that in memory of that evening Cleopatra always wore the odd pearl in her bosom. Octavius found it there after her death. It was in the shape of a tear, an enormous tear, as though all the tears that those beautiful, closed eyes had shed were gathered together in it. Thinking that no woman, not even Livia, was worthy of such a jewel, or fearing that it would bring him misfortune, the conqueror of Actium carried it off as an offering to Venus. "Thus," says Pliny, in melancholy vein, as he was dreaming one day in the temple, "the half of one of those suppers at Alexandria is to-day the ornament of a goddess."

Had Antony forgotten that he was Triumvir? Did he not remember that the life of all men, especially that of a ruler, is a hard and continuous struggle? Not altogether; but, without questioning whether the moment was propitious, unmindful of the disturbing news of troubles in Italy, and of the incursions of the Parthians into Asia Minor, led by the traitor Labismus, he still dallied. He knew that some day he would be forced to take command of his troops, but the life of a conqueror slips by very quickly when he is in the arms of a beautiful woman. While waiting, enmeshed, entangled, like a prey, he was verily a captive; but the bands that held him were too delightful for him to make the slightest effort to break them. When stung by conscience he comforted himself with the reflection that he would know how to get away when it was actually necessary.

In order to have a pretext that would justify his prolonged stay in Alexandria he took up some governmental work, chiefly the revision of the treaty of alliance between the Roman Republic and Cleopatra. All its clauses were arranged in accordance with her wishes and, at her instigation, he sealed it by recognizing Cæsarion as the legitimate son of Cæsar, the heir-presumptive to the throne of Egypt.

The understanding between the two countries being arranged, he summoned the best equipped divisions of his army and had them placed along the borders of the Nile. This military display restored order generally. It was universally recognized that the Queen had a powerful support, and that obedience to her was necessary. Finally, to confirm her authority over these troops, and to show that they were hers to command, the hawk-crest of the Lagidæ was engraved on their shields by the side of the Roman eagle. Armed with helmet and cuirass Cleopatra, riding at Antony's side, reviewed them on the parade ground.

As she was now convinced of the solidity of her throne, and had no longer any uneasiness save the dread of seeing her lover take leave, Cleopatra put her wits to work to keep all disquieting outside cares away from him. Constantly with him, seeing everyone who came near him, she arranged their daily programmes in such fashion that there was no chance for idleness. Their life was a veritable whirlwind. They went for long rides along the sandy roads, taking such unreasonable routes that they returned with their horses foundered. They sought recreation in hunting deer and gazelles, and risked life and limb in pursuit of the wild faun. Danger exhilarated them, and it, in turn, gave them keener appreciation of the hours spent in the privacy of their apartment.

Gradually, however, their sense of enjoyment lost its flavour. The need for perpetual novelty, the desire for sharper sensations, made them seek experiences which were inevitably degrading. In their quest of these new adventures they went, at first secretly, then without disguise, to mix with the disorderly pleasure seekers who nightly frequented the gardens of the Ceramicus.

Many goddesses had temples at Alexandria but none was worshipped more persistently and fervently than Venus. Under the different names of Urania, Astarte, Acidalia, Callypige, and Cypris, each inhabitant, each young girl, recognized her power, and brought her offerings.

In a sycamore grove, opposite the celebrated wall, more than fifteen hundred courtesans trafficked openly in their wares, unhampered by the hypocrisy which restrains modern civilization. Here, also, was the school where expert matrons instructed a hundred young girls in the intricate art of pleasing the goddess of Love. Taken from their parents, either with their consent, or for money, these girls came sometimes from the most remote countries, for the variety of types found at the Ceramicus formed one of its chief attractions. Some were fair, with light eyes and hair like silk; others were of olive complexion, and others again had dark skins. They were not all equally beautiful, that is, according to the Greek ideal, but they all had plump arms and firm breasts, all understood the art of smiling, and of perfuming their bodies.

What did these royal lovers, who had all possible means of gratifying every kind of caprice without leaving their palace walls, what did these misguided beings seek in the dim shade of those trees, among a crowd of loose women?

Unluckily, these expeditions could not be concealed indefinitely. Although Antony wore a mask, and Cleopatra was draped from head to foot in a sombre veil, more than one passer-by, because of the presence of Eros, a devoted satellite of Antony who went everywhere with them, suspected the presence of these sovereigns in places where they had no right to be. The final *dénouement* came as the result of a brawl in which they were hopelessly entangled.

It happened in the Rhakotis quarter, one of the most disreputable parts of the town, where debauchery ran riot. It was filled with houses of ill-repute; the alleys rang with barbarous music accompanying revolting scenes in the fetid taverns. And here the ruler of Rome and the descendant of Egyptian kings loved to spend their nights. Antony was becoming brutalized, and Cleopatra, also, was affected by this life. They quarrelled, passed cynical jests, and, taking colour from their surroundings, nothing pleased Antony so much as to watch the Queen of Egypt seated till morning before these dirty booths, and to hear her ravishing voice, meant to make music for the gods, singing vulgar songs, reciting obscene verses, or using the phrases that he had formerly heard only between low soldiers and women of the town.

One night there was a squabble between one of these women and some sailors. Instantly a tumult of cries and blows began. Violent fighting followed and knives glittered. Cleopatra was about to faint. Her throat was parched, a cold sweat broke out on her forehead. She had hardly strength enough to reach the exit. Eros seized her just in time and carried her into the open air. She revived, but unfortunately her veil had been pushed aside, and pale and frightened appeared the young face that at other times was seen crowned by the head-dress of the Egyptian kings.

What is more significant than the degradation of these lovers, overtaken by Fate? From the crest of Fortune's hill they could have looked down on the ugliness of the world at their feet and have said: "We are safe!" But they were insatiable. Possessing all the best, they coveted the worst as well. They wanted their wheel of sensations to go on turning, turning. At the least sign of its stopping they set it going again, and it dragged them into the depths from which they came up irremediably stained.

This scandal of the street brawl had no immediate consequence, however. The hour of Nemesis had not yet come. The people of Alexandria were content with their reëstablished government, their increased revenue, and attached but little importance to what they called these frivolous pranks. Their own standards were low and there was no actual laws that condemned Cleopatra's conduct. On the contrary, it established a certain sympathy between the Queen and her subjects. Since she, who had seemed so far above them, had descended to the ranks of the street women, what concession might not be expected from her, or what good fortune? Men who had long worshipped her at a distance drew near to regard her with longing eyes. One of these admirers wrote: "Any other woman would grow stale, but not Cleopatra. The more you see her the greater her fascination. She can transform even vice, cruelty, debauchery by her unspeakable charm. In the midst of her excesses the very priests themselves can only bless her!"

Antony also had been adopted by the Alexandrians. Cæsar's aristocratic bearing, his stern expression, his austere habit of mind, had overawed them; while their naturally frivolous temperament was thoroughly at ease in the presence of the jovial Triumvir. Whereas the one always kept them at a distance, whether on horseback or in his litter, never mixing with the populace, the other enjoyed the street shows, went about everywhere, stopped before the stalls, sometimes buying a trifle for which he paid double price, and taking it to Cleopatra. He talked with the men in the street, was not afraid of passing jokes with them, or even of emptying an amphora of wine in their company. He had discarded his military dress when appearing in public, as it recalled the hated Roman rule. He replaced the Roman officers by Egyptian guards, and the coats of mail and helmets, surmounted by silver crests, were exchanged for silk robes with oriental head-dresses.

This delicate flattery of the populace provoked much jesting criticism. "He reserves his tragic rôle for the Romans; for us he has always a smile," many said, recalling the part he had played at the time of the proscriptions.

His intimate associates, who shared this lawless life, had even less cause than the Alexandrians to find fault with him. Like Antony, they were under the bewitching charm of Cleopatra. They loved her, admired her, and to win her favour bore with good humour the sarcastic thrusts of her jesting moods. To please and amuse her some of them sacrificed all sense of dignity. Paterculus has left the story of Munatius Plancus, former consul, and several members of Antony's staff who, one evening during a fête, crowned themselves with reeds, tied fish tails to their naked backs, and mimicked the dance of Glaucus. It seemed as though the masters of the world, those proud Romans who had formerly scorned the Queen of Egypt, had now become her slaves.

VI

Antony's Wives

IT WAS no time for play, for masquerading, or for parades. Threats were in the air. The Parthian invasions were daily becoming bolder and there were many uprisings in Italy. It was one of those feverish crises of that malady which had stricken Italy for more than a century and whose periodic return endangered her foundations. On one hand the landowners were trying to regain their confiscated property; on the other, the war veterans, to whom these estates had been promised, were exacting the fulfilment of the promise. These latter, reinforced by the standing army, which no longer received its pay regularly, were the larger and stronger party. In fact, they were the only remaining organized force of the Republic.

The man who could meet their just demands and enforce his own will would have been master of the situation. With his countless legions and his control over them Antony seemed to be the man. In his absence, Octavius was next in line. But his puny personality and his reputed cowardice and cruelty were grave handicaps. He made sundry efforts to reconcile the opposing parties. On one occasion, at Gabies, he had a meeting of the landowners and representatives of the soldiers to discuss before a jury the relative interests of the opponents. Some decision might have been reached, as both sides desired it, had a hearing been possible; but two people purposely absented themselves; two who were determined on war and had effective means of bringing it about. These two were Fulvia, Antony's wife, and his brother, Lucius.

For Antony was married, very much married. The day after the battle of Pharsalus he had wedded Fulvia, who had already been twice married; the first time to the demagogue Clodius, and, after his tragic death, to Curion, Tribune of the people. In her association with these violent men she had acquired the habit of meddling in politics. Under their influence her mind had become emancipated and masculine; she had lost the sweetness of her own sex without gaining any qualities to make up for it. In spite of this, and although she had no beauty, Fulvia had succeeded in laying hold of the Imperator, perhaps even in making him love her. She had doubtless succeeded, because it was the destiny of this great agitator to upset the hearts of women and yet be subject to their will. Far-seeing and masterful, she had discerned what could be drawn from the powerful instrument that Antony was, provided a firm hand controlled him. The power Fulvia had over him was such that at times he seemed to be nothing more than a sword hung at her girdle.

Her detestable influence was responsible for most of the bloody deeds which have sullied the name of Antony. The three hundred deserters from Brindisi were executed at the instigation of this termagant; their punishment afforded her such keen joy that she desired to be present at the death, that her robe might be spattered with their blood. It was she also who stirred up in her husband's heart his hatred of Cicero.

It is well known with what vehemence Cicero, in his Philippics, denounced the man who, though a Republican, stood for despotism. He designated Antony as "a soldier lacking political genius, without loftiness of soul, destitute of real distinction, lost by debauchery." Divining whose influence impelled Antony to act, he fearlessly accused her: "Is this man free," he demanded of the citizens whom he was urging to quit the demagogic party, "is he free, when controlled by a woman who imposes her laws upon him, prescribes, commands, forbids, as she sees fit?"

Fulvia could never forgive. At the hour of reckoning she found in her venomous heart the arrow that Cicero had planted there, and sent it back with fatal effect. To have her assailant assassinated was not sufficient, she desired to dishonour his remains. When the head of the great orator was brought to Antony, she drew a long gold pin from her hair and pierced the tongue which had defended justice from one end of the world to the other.

Naturally such a woman would not let herself be robbed without protest. When she heard what skilful hands were detaining her husband, rage gnawed at her heart. How should she get him back? Supplications and threats were sent in turn to the Bruchium. But Antony was dwelling in paradise, oblivious to all that did not concern his beautiful mistress. He was determined to remain ignorant of any reason for leaving her and often did not even unroll the scripts which the courier had brought him from his wife.

Fulvia, however, was capable of dire vengeance. To stir up civil war appealed to her as an expedient worthy of consideration. In consultation with her brother-in-law, Lucius, an intriguer who had the dream of crushing Octavius and putting his own family in power, she said: "When thousands of men are dying for his cause Antony will be compelled to leave Cleopatra's arms."

At the instigation of the two conspirators several landowners roused the rural population. There were skirmishes and combats. A large number of towns declared themselves as opposed to Octavius. The cries of death resounded as far as Rome. The statues of the Triumvirs were broken. Lucius took advantage of these uprisings to declare himself, in his brother's name, the defender of Republican ideals. Antony himself, he affirmed, thought that the Triumvirate had lasted long enough. He was ready to cancel his power and content himself with being Consul.

These assertions gained many partisans for him among the men who wished law and order restored. With things at such a pass it was incredible that Antony would not come to assume the leadership. Delegates sent to Alexandria to induce him to return were refused admission to his presence. Cleopatra bade them depart without delay on pain of imprisonment.

Hearing of this outrage, Fulvia, whom no crime appalled, conceived the idea of combining with Antony's enemies. She made a proposal to Octavius, and, as a proof of sincerity, suggested his marrying Clodia, her daughter by Clodius. She was a charming young girl, not yet seventeen years of age, and had already attracted Octavius's fancy. But he was not to be ensnared; at no price would this practical man have encumbered his career by having Fulvia for a mother-in-law!

So the war went on.

Despite Antony's contempt for his adversary—"that beardless blackguard," as he scornfully called him—he knew very well what the ultimate issue would be, although Cleopatra took all possible means to conceal the actual danger; but he persisted in his indifference. His exasperated wife was in despair and, seeing the peril increase from day to day, began to re-open negotiations. However difficult these might be with such an elusive husband, still they offered the only possible chance of rousing Antony to action. The chief thing was to find an ambassador who could gain an audience.

She and Lucius finally selected Ahenobarbus, the Triumvir's old comrade-in-arms, one of his bravest generals, who during all their campaigns together had rendered most valuable aid, yet at the hour of victory had always effaced himself before his chief. He, at least, would be given a hearing.

When this Roman of the old school, fresh from the battlefield, whose cuirass seemed to stick to his body as his flesh to his bones, entered the luxurious perfumed quarters of the Bruchium, and saw Antony in a flowing, embroidered robe, a scimitar in his girdle, his head wrapped in a turban adorned with a shining carbuncle, he was overcome. Was this the conqueror of Philippi, his comrade that he had not seen since, clad in wild beasts' skins, he had endured without complaint the bitter hardships of a Macedonian winter?

"Mark Antony!" he exclaimed, and that name alone expressed all the astonishment and dismay that filled his soul.

Antony was far from callous to this appeal. When he understood what his wife and brother had undertaken, his face reddened. He knew well that personal interest and profit formed part of their zeal in serving him; but the fact remained that Fulvia furnished a rare example of wifely devotion, and Lucius was an intelligent man. For the moment he had a sincere desire to join them.

"If you feel that way," said Ahenobarbus with the simplicity of a heart accustomed to match deeds with words, "why hesitate? The men who are fighting for your cause are imprisoned in the fort at Perugia; they are in danger of starving to death. Take command of your legions and go to their aid."

But things were not so simple as this brave soldier imagined. Cleopatra undertook to enlighten him. Little versed as he was in the ways of sentiment, he comprehended at the first sight of her, at the sound of her charming voice, that Antony was no longer his own master, that he belonged body and soul to this siren. And then he tried to make her see reason.

He explained the situation without reserve. If

Lucius and Fulvia were dependent on their own resources, Octavius would probably have the advantage, and Antony would lose the chance of overcoming an enemy who, though cowardly now, might one day be formidable.

Cleopatra was too wise not to realize the justice of these arguments. No one was more anxious than she for Antony's advancement, no one had greater reason to dread the triumph of that legitimate nephew, who disputed with Cæsarion the heritage of Cæsar. Undoubtedly if Lucius had been alone in his struggle, she would have said: "For our mutual glory, for the extension of our power, go to the front." But giving Antony his liberty, permitting her cherished lover to set foot on Italian soil, meant giving him up to Fulvia. Ugly, coarse, and antipathetic though she was, better fitted to harangue troops than to inspire passion, nevertheless this Bellona caused her a certain uneasiness. She knew her ambitions and was perfectly conscious of her despotic control of Antony. Under these conditions was it prudent, even for a few days, to deliver this precious hostage into her hands? Weighing all considerations, Love, that tyrant who knows no will save his own, gained his end. Perugia, Rome, the whole of Italy might be burning, Cleopatra would not give up her lover.

The day before Ahenobarbus, disappointed and disgusted, was to return to Italy, a trifling incident changed the course of things. Antony was depressed. His conscience troubled him; that conscience which he had ignored so long, but which, at certain memories, disturbed his peace. His old war comrade said nothing more, but his looks were full of reproach.

"How shall I divert him?" thought Cleopatra. "What amusement can I devise to protect him during this last day from the appeals of Ahenobarbus?"

She proposed a fishing party.

Both men accepted and the boats across the canal which led to the harbour of Eunostus, carried them to Lake Mareotis. The reeds were rustling in the breeze, above the quiet water stretched a heaven of radiant blue. The buildings along the shore made red reflections in the lake as though they were on fire. The vessels anchored at the further end of the lake where, remote from noise and excitement, the carp had taken refuge in the quiet lapping of the waves.

Antony threw his line half a dozen times and caught nothing. This bad luck, especially before Ahenobarbus, who was watching him with folded arms, increased his ill-humour. Irritated and determined to catch the fish, or at least to seem to catch them, he whispered a word to Eros. What he told him was to fasten to his own hook one of the largest fish that had been caught and to slip it skilfully under the water so that no one would suspect the trick.

The Queen, however, was not long fooled. She, too, knew how to play that game. She quickly concocted a plan that, unknown to Eros, another attendant carried out.

Antony was again in high spirits. Every time he drew in his line a large carp hung from his hook. He was overwhelmed with compliments on his astounding skill. All at once, just as he drew out a huge prize, there was a burst of laughter. The fish, this time, proved to be one that had been kept in brine to serve as bait. Ordinarily Antony would have been the first to join in the ridicule against himself, but in the presence of the dignified Roman general he was annoyed and mortified. The party went home in silence.

Thinking this a good chance for a final effort, Ahenobarbus waited until everyone had gone to his own apartment and then sought Antony.

"Do you not realize that this is no place for you?" he demanded. "This child's play is fit only for women and eunuchs; but you, warrior, chief of the State, one of the three heads of the Republic, when there are towns and continents waiting for your taking. . . ."

With the gesture habitual to him in moments of perplexity, Antony put his elbow on his knee, his chin resting in his right hand, and stared at his friend. What was there to say? That fire that still burned in his veins flamed up, showing him the glorious goal toward which they had marched together.

"I wish I might follow you!" he cried.

"What is there to hinder you?"

"How can you ask!"

"Is love so mighty then," gasped the old soldier, "that once in its thrall a man has no more power over himself?"

They continued to talk. Antony was ready to be persuaded. The light wound to his vanity made him sensitive to appeals to his honour. The future spread out before him. Where would the life of a love-sick satrap lead him?

Suddenly he cried, grasping his friend's hand: "You are right; to-morrow I will go with you." And with a firm step he turned toward Cleopatra's bedchamber.

She was lying on a low couch, awaiting her lover, but she was more than usually eager for his coming this evening. He had been morose at supper. What had been the trouble? Was he annoyed at the joke she had played on him?

Charmian was beside her, trying to comfort her. Surely Antony understood a joke!

The soothing sound of the sea came in through the windows. Just outside the curtain of her room Antony heard the question: "Do you believe he will always love me?"

His heart was softened and he thought: "How can I hurt the most tender of women?" Going in, he looked at her without speaking, and she asked:

"What is it? Of what are you thinking?"

He hesitated. Then, suddenly, like one who takes his courage in both hands, he cried:

"Beyond all question I must go away."

She looked at him, incredulous. This was worse than all her fears.

"Go away! You are saying it to frighten me, because I teased you."

"Child," he ejaculated, "as though such a thing counted! I owe it to those who are fighting for me."

Cleopatra's heart sank.

"You wish to be with your wife!"

In spite of the gravity of the occasion Antony could not help laughing.

"You! Jealous of Fulvia!"

After all, why should she not be jealous? The cause which this deserted wife was heading was not led by an ordinary woman. Beautiful or hideous, with their storms, their upheavals, their tears, these passionate souls are the most dangerous rivals. Cleopatra understood; she knew, better than any other woman, of what the heart is capable to protect or regain its loved one. And Antony's temperament did not reassure her. At a distance from her, he would surely find in that other woman, that Amazon, the very support that his wavering will unconsciously sought in all his relations with women.

All these soul-torturing thoughts she put in her next demand:

"You want me to die, then?" And, as though she were already nearing death, she fell back on her pillows, pale and sobbing.

That was enough to shake his new-born resolution. Antony was already wavering. Bending over that dear face, which he had so often seen flushed with happiness, his only thought was to repair the damage his words had wrought. He would not leave her at once. He would get Ahenobarbus to take his place and later, should it be necessary . . .

Cleopatra recovered immediately!

"If it were necessary," she whispered, still trembling, and pressing his head against her bosom, "I should be the first to urge you to go. I desire your well-being, your glory far more than you do. But, believe me, your wife and your brother are fools. They are working only for their own interest. Let them get out of this embarrassment, which they have brought about themselves, without any aid from you."

Antony was more than content to believe her. And that night there was no further question of their parting.

Other happy nights followed. The lovers were reunited, and behind those protecting ramparts that love builds they were oblivious of war, threats, everything. What matter if the world fell, so long as they were together?

The gods, however, who favoured Antony, combined this time to save him. At the moment when Perugia, exhausted, was on the point of surrendering; when the army, headed by his brother and his wife, seeing no chance of the Triumvir's coming, began to lose courage, Fulvia suddenly fell ill and died. She had been the soul of the resisting army. With this support gone Lucius was not strong enough to continue the fight against such heavy odds, and he sheathed his sword. Thus, by unforeseen events, Antony's absence, which had seemed so fatal, brought most excellent results. He had taken no part in the war and so could not be held responsible for it. Consequently there would be no difficulty in making peace with Octavius. He had only to disavow any political designs of his own. But he must at least go to negotiate this affair in person.

With Fulvia dead there was no further reason for

Cleopatra to oppose Antony's temporary absence, or to feel any alarm in regard to it. She had borne him one child and another was coming. They had decided to celebrate their wedding in the spring and to legitimatize the children, as Cæsar had done in the case of Cæsarion. As though, however, the growlings of the crafty beast that lurks near perfect happiness were heard from afar, Cleopatra still had certain apprehensions. What did she dread? She could not have defined it. The idea of consulting the oracles came to her. Perhaps they would explain that mysterious danger against which her whole being rebelled.

Here, as at Rome, the long-bearded augurs sought to unravel the secrets of the future by studying the sacred books, observing the flight of birds and examining the entrails of the victims. As Claros, Cumes, and Tibur had their sybils, Delphi her Pythian priestess, so Alexandria had a college of celebrated astrologers. These famous men not only gave their nights to the study of the heavens (they knew the laws that governed the stars and they gave the constellations the names that they bear today) but their science pretended to be able to question these stars and to obtain information from them. Each celestial body represented a divinity who influenced the birth and life of mortals, and its vivid brilliancy in the height of happiness was dimmed by the approach of disaster.

After nightfall, when it was entirely dark, Cleopatra, accompanied by a slave, climbed the one hundred and twenty steps which led to the highest terrace.

Sisogenus, the great compiler of horoscopes, who had been advised of her visit, was awaiting her. With outstretched arms and his forehead in the dust he saluted her three times.

"What does the daughter of Amoun-Ra seek of an insignificant being?"

She explained her wish to know the destiny of Mark Antony. In a few days the Triumvir would be in Latin territory once more. What fate awaited him there? Was there anything to fear in regard to him?

Before replying, the sage, draped in yellow, his sleeves and high cap adorned with a row of bells which rang as he moved, traced some signs on the sand of the terrace; then, in an attitude of ecstasy, his body bent back, his palms outspread, he searched the starry vault. Myriads of golden points pricked the sombre blue, and their reflections in the sea were like a shower of diamonds.

Sisogenus suddenly seized his wand and pointed to a star. He had recognized the planet under which Antony was born.

"There!" he cried, "clear and brilliant it is approaching its zenith."

But presently the star grew dim. It drew near another star. A moment later the latter seemed to fade away and the first shone again in its original, magnificent splendour.

Cleopatra was much impressed by this phenomenon, the more so on hearing that it was Octavius's star which had made Antony's pale. This experience was conclusive. It was undeniably true that by their natures these two men were opposed to each other, and that Antony should, in all matters, distrust his colleague and avoid him.

When she brought him the horoscope Antony was the more impressed by it because of a vision which had disturbed his slumber. In his dream he had been walking in a field of flowers. All at once he had a sensation of resistance, as though a barrier had been placed in his path. After a hard struggle he waked suddenly, covered with sweat, as though he had just escaped some grave peril.

Antony would not have been of his age and country if he had ignored such a warning. No Latin was indifferent to these things. A sneeze, a burning of the ears, had their meaning. A fall, the swelling of the little finger, were regarded as evil omens. If he saw a flight of crows on leaving the house, the prudent man returned home and carried out no business that day. If, on the contrary, a swarm of bees welcomed him as he stepped out into the golden sunshine, he was safe in any undertaking, for they brought good luck!

Naturally, when such importance was attached to insignificant things, the signs of the heavens were pregnant with meaning. If Antony had deferred his going it would have brought only unhappiness to Cleopatra and himself, for stronger than all dreams was a voice which warned them that the better part of their romance was over. Would they ever again find time to give themselves up entirely to the joys of love? That careless rapture which passionate youth brings was ended. Different obligations would separate them, perhaps indefinitely. Antony's position called him back to his duty. That peace with Octavius, if it were accomplished, would solve only one of the new difficulties which had arisen. The Parthians had to be subdued, order must be established in Asia Minor; many things demanded his attention. Already, with the putting on of his armour, the Imperator felt like his old self; he heard the clarion call with pleasure and his gay, child-like smile had vanished. He left his cup half filled with wine.

Cleopatra was unhappy; she had more to dread from the coming separation. A sorrowful expression came into her eyes when she looked at her lover, and, in spite of herself, in spite of his repeated promises that he would return before the end of the year, bitter grief wrung her heart.

When the day came, although she was faint from weeping, she insisted on going down to the ship with him. A fresh wind was coming up from the east. The ruffled sea was covered with long white wings, wings which would carry off her happiness. If she could only keep him with her! But poor human desires have never for a single moment deferred the coming disaster. The ship's sails were set; the three ranks of rowers had taken their places, and fifty ebony arms were about to strike the water. Leaning over the edge of the rampart, which ran along the side of the *Heptastadium,* Cleopatra was repeating softly the tender farewells which her hand waved to Antony. Just as the ship left the quay she cried:

"Remember the stars!"

If Antony had been torn at this time by the revengeful passion which inflamed him the day after the Ides of March, or by the hate which possessed him later—too late—and which was to set him, weakened, against an enemy who had grown powerful, he would undoubtedly have gained the mastery of Octavius, and the fate of the world would have been changed. But the time that he had spent at Alexandria had sapped his primitive instincts, and the fighting power that was one of the savage beauties of his nature had lost its freshness. Instead of returning to Italy with the fierce enthusiasm essential to victory, his mind was absorbed in Egyptian magic; his chief idea was to bring about peace as quickly as possible so that he might be free to go back.

Octavius, also, wanted an amicable adjustment of the disturbances which the family Antonius had brought about, but from totally different motives. He was occupied with more serious things. Pompey was in command of several legions who were bound to him through loyalty to the glorious memory of his father. He had taken these to Sardinia and was superintending the piracy of a fleet whose object was to starve out the Latin coasts. If Antony, with the sixteen legions which he had in Macedonia, and the fast fleet which the Rhodians had built for him, were to form an alliance with this new antagonist, Octavius would inevitably be defeated.

It is a truism that fear makes men both cruel and cowardly. In the present instance it caused Octavius to take outrageous reprisals from the vanquished Perugians and made him a lamb in the presence of Antony. He had never been really at ease with his herculean colleague. All that Antony stood for in beauty, pride, and happiness was secret gall and bitterness to him. Though quite as well versed in debauchery, his weakness made him despair of ever attaining the graceful, easy bearing which made Antony so attractive. He felt, too, the indifference of his soldiers toward him, compared with the feeling that his opponent inspired among his men; their devotion was such that they preferred serving under him without pay to being well paid for marching against him. Feeling the scantiness of his ammunition, compared with Antony's abundant resources, he had concluded at the outset that it would be wiser to have Antony for a friend than an enemy, and to-day again he said to himself: "Though it cost me the one hundred million sesterces that he has stolen from the heritage of Cæsar, yet I will make this man my ally."

Both sides then were ready to come to terms. Their followers were as eager for it as the chief combatants themselves, for after so much grief, agitation, and bloodshed, all the world thirsted for peace.

Antony's friends were awaiting him at Brindisi. They had no difficulty in persuading him to repulse the revolutionary proposals of Pompey and to come to an understanding with Octavius. This latter offered Cyrenaica, which had been included in Lepidus's share, in exchange for Gaul, which originally had been allotted to Antony in the division of territory.

Anxious to go to Asia, where his most important interests lay, Antony selected Asinius Pollion to look after his affairs in Italy. The latter's tact and knowledge qualified him to deal with Mæcenas, Octavius's delegate, and Antony gave him full power. It would be time to sign the papers when he returned from Asia.

Antony's haste to plant his eagles in the Orient was because Cleopatra had persuaded him to regard these provinces as their common property, the rich area that was destined to supplant ancient, impoverished Europe and to become that world-empire which they had planned to establish together. To drive out the Parthians and procure the gold necessary to content his soldiers, who were his chief support, was of infinitely greater importance than to dispute fragments of territory with Octavius and Lepidus. Antony, as always when impelled by his strong instinct as a leader, showed his usual masterful decision, quickness, and courage. He immediately took Palestine from Pacoros and reëstablished Herod there; punished the towns which had massacred their garrisons, put Labienus to flight, destroyed the gates of Lamanos, and took possession of Syria. These victories recalled the days of his untrammelled youth, and roused that enthusiastic energy which so often followed his periods of inertia.

His friends, knowing this complete metamorphosis, had reckoned accordingly. They persuaded him to put on his Imperator's cuirass while they were laying the cornerstone of a new Triumvirate, saying among themselves: "We shall gain time in this way"; for they had their own plans. They thought that a marriage would serve the double purpose of making the desired treaty binding and also would keep him from going back to his mistress;

so they had arranged to bring about a union between him and the sister of Octavius. They knew that although death had fortunately taken away Fulvia, the main obstacle had not gone with her. They understood perfectly that "the courtesan of the Nile," as in their hate and scorn they designated Cleopatra, was still there, beguiling, regal, clothed with her indescribable charm. But absence, for the time being, lessened her power, and by this absence they were determined to profit.

Antony's return was the propitious moment to bring about the union of the two Triumvirs by means of the most pleasing of women. The important thing was to arrange this skilfully and without undue haste. The sun on that day shone over Rome not with the metallic brilliance which cut hard outlines in the Levantine landscape, but gently, delicately, with fleece-like clouds that softened the light. Among its flowery hills the ancient city lay in quiet dignity; its low houses clustered around its temples seemed like a family group.

From the first moment that Antony trod the streets, filled with sacred memories; when, on the border of the river, he looked again at the place where he had gathered the ashes of Cæsar from the funeral pyre; when he heard the great voices of the Forum welcoming him—his heart quivered with an emotion that he had not felt for a long time. Whatever joys might thrill him elsewhere, no other place in the world could give him the inexpressible happiness of feeling that he was at home. Rome, it was the birthplace of his fathers; the air that he breathed there stirred and exhilarated him like that on a mountain top. The blood ran through his veins richer, fuller, as though all that of his forebears had joined the flood.

In this frame of mind Octavia's attractions were naturally very powerful. Although not radiantly beautiful, her modest, winning carriage represented all that to the Latin mind signified the guardian of the home. Her face was oval, rather long, the type which the artists of the Renaissance chose in painting their Madonnas. Her dreamy eyes were shaded by long lashes, and her masses of hair, whose regular braids encircled her forehead, rested there like a crown.

No more striking contrast could have been found than that between this sweet, gracious woman and the implacable Fulvia; unless in comparing the warm seductions of Cleopatra with the diaphanous delicacy, the sensitive shadows, which enveloped the sister of Octavius.

The young woman had been married once. The short time that she had lived with Marcellus, for whom she still wore a widow's veil, had been filled with love, peace, and fruitfulness, and was indicative of what life would be at her side. It was on her discretion and deep-seated kindliness that the friends of Antony and Octavius alike had relied, hoping to make of her arms an arch of peace which would unite the two columns of the world. Her domestic virtues alone would have insured its solidity. At a time when baseness was rampant, when selfish fear engendered cowardice, when treason entered even into the heart of family life, she had many times shown her intrinsic qualities, her generous, human, kindly soul. Her gentle influence over her brother had frequently saved the victims of his wrath. Her friend, Tullia, owed the life of Thoranius, her idolized husband, to her intervention. He had been sentenced to death more than a month and was awaiting the hour of his execution. All Tullia's prayers had been in vain and the time was at hand. What could be done to save the unfortunate man? Public opinion was not in favour of his condemnation, but, debased as it was, what means could it take to express its disapproval? Octavia was fearless. One evening when the Imperator was expected at the theatre, she prepared a device. At the moment when he entered his box, dressed in purple and surrounded by lictors, a curtain rose and by the side of a young woman weeping there appeared a phantom loaded with chains. Cries of "Mercy, mercy," resounded on every side. What each individual would have feared to ask, the crowd demanded. The future Augustus was too weak to go counter to the voice of the people. He raised his right hand. The cause was won!

Octavia's presence had the effect on Antony of grateful shade. Never since childhood had he been associated with such a wholesome, comforting personality. The idea of making his home with her gave him a qualm of conscience. If only he had met her earlier he would undoubtedly have been a different man. His way of living would not have become so debased. But, as he was to-day, how could he change his habits? How reach her level? Deluded by an apparently newly gained liberty, he said to himself: "Who knows, it may not be too late!" The next moment the image of the Egyptian sorceress came to him, forbidding any happiness save with her in the alternate fever and ecstasy which her love created.

Octavia was thoroughly familiar with Mark Antony's past life. Desirous, as he was, of combining their political interests, her brother, who was devoted to her, had not concealed from her the risks involved in a marriage with Cleopatra's lover. He could not bring himself to praise a man so entirely opposite in character to himself. Fundamentally honest and careful of her future as Octavia was, she might, by these warnings, have been spared such a perilous adventure; but she had a brave heart under her outward shyness. Her youth longed to taste the sweets of passion as well as the quiet joys of life. From their very first interview she had been irresistibly drawn toward the tyrant that Antony was to be in her life. It would not be possible, she thought while admiring his splendid contour and his bright smile, for such a man to be false. If he had yielded to temptations it was because those near him had failed to bind him with that cord of tenderness which can restrain the lion. This was the pathetic mistake of virtue, confident of its own power; that fatal attraction which makes gentle hearts the prey of strong, full-blooded men, and impels them to yield to those who will become their masters and their ruin.

Octavia's illusion continued for some time. The marriage began auspiciously with that real happiness which was unknown to Antony and afforded him pleasure by its novelty. In his wife's eyes, he was a traveller who had seen many countries, destroyed many forests, and whose wounded feet were grateful for repose. He had exchanged his flaming paradise for this innocent love in which he was a novice, and for some time he was happy in the new experience. As to his young wife, she felt that the charm of completed cycles was hers, and that she had found the secret which makes the spring sweet and gives fragrance to the flowers. Her heart was full to overflowing and she had no other desire than to fulfil her husband's lightest wish. With instinctive knowledge, she divined his thought and carried out his fancy before he had time even to stretch out his hand. One day when they were walking together he admired the palace that Pompey had built on the Appian Way and expressed regret that so beautiful a place remained empty. She immediately obtained permission from her brother to have the ban lifted and offered the palace, filled with its wonderful treasures, to Antony. Although her own tastes up to the present moment had been simple, she thought no frame too spacious or too rich for her husband. How could this Omphale, consumed with faithful devotion, foresee that this palace would seem a prison to Antony before the first year of their marriage had gone by?

Her tenderness and devotion were so all-absorbing that the atmosphere soon became stifling to Antony, who felt that his arms were wide enough to embrace an infinity of delights. Full of strength and imagination, this grandson of Hercules felt cramped in the network of tradition, and Rome, which had looked so magnificent on the day of his triumphal return, had taken again its real proportions, which, in comparison with the magnificence of Alexandria's sumptuous buildings, obelisks, and columns, seemed like those of a market town. Its austere customs, narrow views, and prejudices irritated him. Antony was bored. What had become of those joyous songs whose golden-winged fancies had cradled his life in the past two years?

The association with Octavius was intolerable. Whereas the men who had brought about their reconciliation were delighted at seeing them apparently working together in harmony, issuing decrees, reviewing troops, or united at the family table, they themselves were conscious of a fermenting mutual hatred. It was inevitable between two men equal in rank, sharing an authority which caused perpetual friction. Whether acting for the State, or in the smallest detail of private life, everything was a subject of dispute. When the Roman people, emotional and easily excited, applauded one or the other of the Triumvirs, or showed the least sign of approval of his acts, the demon of jealousy arose. Even the games, in which they sometimes sought diversion, led to disagreements, for neither of the two could stand having the other one win. The dice on several occasions having been favourable to Antony, Octavius claimed that they were loaded. One evening they entertained their guests with a pair of fighting cocks, and the customary stakes were laid. Once, twice, three times Octavius's cock won. Antony was white with rage. He left the room abruptly and even Octavia's pleading was powerless to bring him back that evening.

Trifling as such wounds were, their daily occurrence was like mosquito bites which finally poison the entire system. Their relations, never cordial, grew definitely worse. Antony showed always the more decided enmity. Confident, as he was, that the first place should belong to him, he was irritated by any interference, especially when Octavius was given precedence over him. Upon the least pretext the words of the Egyptian oracle would come back to him: "Keep away from your rival. Whenever you come together your star will be eclipsed by his. In the Orient alone will your star have its full radiance."

Even had he tried to forget these ominous words, the diviners, astrologers, all the clique with which Cleopatra had secretly surrounded him, kept them constantly in his mind. The longing to get away from this annoying comparison haunted him. His one object was to leave Rome and return to the land where he could find that preëminence so indispensable to his masterful nature. To be the chief, the one whose commands all the world obeyed! To look out on unlimited space and to say to himself: "No one can contend with me for the tiniest morsel of it!" Those dreams which pride evolves to tempt the covetous mind!

Only a great victory could upset the equality of power and exalt one of the Triumvirs above the other two. This Antony determined to win. The colossal vision of making the Orient his military and political centre, and of founding an immense empire of which he would be the sole sovereign, appealed to him more than ever. It was reviving Cæsar's chimera, that chimera which, in an age where venality reigned, would supply him gold in abundance. But could he carry it out to a glorious victory? To begin with, he must expel the Parthian invaders who infested the frontiers, then establish himself beyond the Euphrates and gain the mastery of Persia.

The plans for this daring campaign were already drawn; they had been laid out in the minutest details by the conqueror of Gaul. Antony, who had been in Cæsar's confidence during his latter days, had only to take possession of them. The only change that he needed to make was in the choice of a city to supplant Rome. Alexandria apparently had been selected by Cæsar, who on the eve of this great enterprise had been wholly absorbed in Cleopatra. This same Alexandria had shone in Antony's eyes as his future capital while he was with Cleopatra and they were elaborating their plans. But to-day, in the house ruled by the virtuous Octavia, even the name of Egypt was abhorrent. He thought of Athens.

Like all women really in love, Octavia would rather have kept her husband at her side. To lean on his breast was happiness enough for her tender heart. When Antony unfolded his ambitious projects she felt as though joy were about to leave her fireside for ever, and that the future held for her only sorrow and disappointment. But she was too sensible not to realize that action is the law of great lives, and that to love a conqueror entails lonely melancholy.

Even her brother, enamoured as he was of his

bride, Livia, pricked by this spur of supremacy, had just left to do battle with the pirates of Sextus Pompey. Octavia accepted Antony's departure like a submissive wife, but exacted a promise that after the birth of her child he would allow her to join him in Greece.

A sensation of escape, such as a ship feels when freed from her moorings, thrilled Antony's heart the moment he passed the mole and saw the port of Ostia growing fainter in the distance. He was free. In vain he tried to repress this feeling of exultation. It was useless. He remembered his wife's gracious goodness, the love she showered on him, the real affection that he had for her, and he was filled with self-reproach. But he could not control his delight; he was enchanted to have loosed his shackles. To be back again in the fight, to be working out his own destiny, was like waking up after a long spell of drowsiness.

Athens afforded him the exquisite pleasure of being the cynosure of all eyes; the delight of receiving, without having to share them, the keys of power; its submission, its homage. The Greeks had preserved an indelible memory of his personality. They admired his beauty, his military genius, his strength. A warrior primarily, they knew him also as a patron of art who respected their traditions. His pilgrimage to the summit of the Acropolis, made on foot and clothed in the national pallium, had endeared him to all hearts. Whatever reports had come to them since, their original conviction was unaltered: Mark Antony was a demigod. They lavished titles and honours upon him. A chorus of dancing girls offered him the thyrsus of Bacchus crowned with leaves, and fêtes were held everywhere, as at the celebration of the Nabathæans. This delirium of flattery passed all bounds and ended in absurdity. They offered this new Bacchus the hand of the virgin Athene who stood before the Parthenon, armed with the gold helmet and lance of the Olympian games.

Antony, secretly amused, pretended to take this seriously.

"I will accept this offer of marriage," he said, "provided my spouse brings me a million drachmas."

The sycophants were caught in the trap. They carried on the game. It was a severe lesson, however, and one of them, the High Priest charged with supplying this money from the treasury of the temple, could not restrain himself from saying: "Zeus himself did not demand so much to become the lover of your mother, Semele!"

In the whirl of these extravagant espousals Octavia was apparently forgotten; but she made no protest. There is distinction in sharing honours with a goddess. She only asked to be allowed to come and play her part in the comedy. The Athenians were no fools. They received her enthusiastically, and pretended to honour her as the living image of Athene. There were festivals, entertainments, banquets, and in order to make them as gorgeous as he desired Antony had only to copy those that he had revelled in at Alexandria. Once again he was living the life of an Oriental sovereign and, robed in purple, shod with sandals of gold, his forehead bound with fillets, he employed his leisure time in presiding over the athletic games, watching the races and wrestling matches, the lance- and disc-throwing. Octavia awarded the prizes, and happy, united, with no thought of the morrow, they both enjoyed their gracious sovereignty.

Spring had come again. Antony watched the budding branches of the sacred laurel and drank of the fountain of Clepsydra. The oracles that he had consulted had promised him a triumph. He was eager to take his place at the head of the troops, who, under the command of Ventidius, were awaiting him in Epirus.

The campaign opened brilliantly. A succession of uninterrupted victories by the advance-guard seemed to indicate that the invasion of Persia would be simply a military procession. Success at this time meant all the more because Octavius was then fighting his own battles on the shores of Sicily.

These were golden hours for Antony; hours when the thought "The world with its kingdoms will be mine," came to him repeatedly. This illusion made him careless in replying to messages from his brother-in-law. Secure himself, he was rejoicing in the difficulties of Octavius and had no desire whatever to send to his assistance the noble Rhodian fleet for which he was clamouring.

Octavia felt very differently. If her passionate love had thrown her into Antony's arms, it had in no way lessened her warm affection for her brother. Her loyalty, even had she not cared for Octavius, would have made her remember that one of the chief reasons for her marriage with Antony had been to forward the interests of both. Up to the present time she had only been called upon to adjust slight disagreements between them. To-day, however, conditions were different; indeed, the very supremacy of the two rulers was at stake. They envied each other, they hated each other, and between these opposing forces her gentle personality was in imminent danger of being crushed. Why had the gods so cruelly put this grain of wheat between two millstones?

After driving out Antiochus, Antony returned from Syria. He was drunk with the exultation of victory and his wife decided that this would be a propitious moment to present her petition to him. She went to Ephesus to meet him, accompanied by Ahenobarbus, who deplored the dissension between the Triumvirs and predicted dire consequences. Antony's first greeting was so full of affection that she was led to believe that her influence over the conqueror was not wholly lost. With the tenderest caution, but firmly, as her conscience demanded, she asked why he still kept the fleet in the harbour instead of despatching it to her brother's assistance. Quite apart from their signed contract, was he unmindful of the fact that *he* might have need of reinforcements in the heart of Asia, even as Octavius was needing these ships? This refusal to send one might later cut him off from the other. Why did they not coöperate?

Her eminently rational appeal made little impression on Antony, for he felt himself invincible. He knew that a rupture was inevitable, and left to himself he probably would have brought it about at once, but he was touched by Octavia's tears. He had always been easily moved by women, and after yielding to those who made tempestuous demands upon him, it seemed only fair that, for once in his life, he should heed this messenger of peace.

"Go," he commanded, "make terms with Octavius, but remember, before all else, that you are the wife of Antony!"

Greater difficulties than she had looked for awaited her in arranging matters with her brother. Exasperated by the evidently evil intentions of Antony, he decided that such an ally was as dangerous as an enemy, and that while awaiting the supreme decision it was as well to learn to be independent. Aided by Agrippa, who was showing his authority on all maritime matters, he commenced to build a fleet. The port of Tarentum was full of excitement. Well-paid carpenters and caulkers were busy night and day, singing as they worked. The noise of hammers and hatchets resounded. The rhythmic ringing of the anvil was broken by the cries of the fishmongers and bargemen.

It was in the midst of this strenuous labour that Octavia arrived to hold conference with her brother. As she drew near, he was surrounded by engineers to whom he was giving endless orders, and the welcome he accorded her was, unlike his usual greeting, defiant rather than cordial.

"What do you wish? Why are you here?"

"I am only a little ahead of the fleet which Antony has put at your disposal."

"It is too late," replied Octavius curtly, "in three months my own ships will be on the high seas."

That first repulse was hard to bear. It killed the hope of bringing about a reconciliation which Octavia had built on her brother's embarrassments. But she was not a woman to be easily baulked. The mission that she had undertaken filled her with invincible courage and tenacity. Through life and death she would carry it out. She now defended her husband's actions as valiantly as she had those of her brother when pleading with her husband. If Antony had delayed, it was because he had been surrounded by such countless difficulties that he had lost count of time. The moment that she had reminded him of the need for action he had answered: "I am ready to go." He would be there in a few days.

But the deeply furrowed brow of Octavius, marked with premature wrinkles between his black eyebrows, was not so easily smoothed as Antony's had been. The masterful will which enveloped them both like a cuirass had no fissure in his case. Octavia saw that her efforts to defend her husband were futile, and as her excuses had really little foundation she began to plead her own cause.

"If you give way to anger," she said, looking tenderly at her brother, "if sword and lance cross, no one can tell who will be the victor. There is only one certainty and that is that I, wife or sister of the vanquished, will spend the rest of my life in tears!"

Was he touched by this woman's gentle plea? Or did he in the bottom of his heart feel that if he repulsed Antony's advances the latter would ally himself with their mutual enemy Sextus Pompey?

Be that as it may, urged by his two good geniuses, Agrippa and Mæcenas, Octavius yielded and consented to an agreement.

Anchored in the bay of Piræus, Antony was awaiting his brother-in-law's decision. As soon as he got the report from Ahenabarbus he set sail with the two hundred and twenty triremes which were his pride and his strength. Their arrival at Tarentum had a tremendous effect. When Octavius first caught sight of them in the distance, their snowy sails seeming to cover the face of the waters, enveloped in the silvery foam splashed up by the oars, he had the conviction that however numerous and powerful his own future fleet might be, these splendid ships, all new, well equipped, and well armed, would be a most valuable addition to his navy.

But he could not foresee that those same ships, those slender craft, would one day turn against Antony and decide the victory of Actium. And Antony, still wrapped in his own illusions, had no power to look so far into the future. In his ardour to begin that famous campaign through which he expected to be the master of the world, he was absorbed in his dreams of the six Gallic legions, made up of expert archers, trained foot-soldiers, strong cavalrymen, that he was to obtain in exchange for part of his fleet.

The negotiations were long and complicated, as each side desired to secure the greatest possible benefit from the arrangement and accord a minimum in return. Unaided by the gentle Octavia, who went back and forth bearing the olive branch, it is doubtful if they would ever have come to an understanding. While Agrippa and Mæcenas on one side, and Ahenobarbus and Pollion on the other, discussed, dissected, picked over, one by one, the ships and soldiers that constituted the coin of that terrible market, a plaintive refrain could be heard.

"War, more war!" groaned Octavia, "will you transform me from the happiest woman in the world to the most miserable?" And regularly every morning she went to the temple of Vesta, where she lighted at the sacred candelabra as many tapers as there were prayers in her heart.

In granting the prayers of the loving sister and faithful wife, the goddess softened the hearts of the two adversaries. Each having weighed the relative advantage that he would gain by certain concessions, they both assumed a grand air of magnanimity. They pretended that neither of them wanted to grieve the one who formed such a close bond between them and that her little hand should disarm them. A new agreement was made, prolonging the Triumvirate for five years. This modern Sabine woman in raising the golden cup to drink to them that evening, might truthfully have said: "I have preserved the peace of the world!"

VII

The Marriage at Antioch

LEANING on the parapet, within sound of the waves that lapped against the quai, Cleopatra watched the ship that was carrying off her lover grow smaller in the distance. When the highest mast had disappeared beneath the horizon, she let her hand fall; the hand that had been waving a handkerchief since the ship had weighed anchor. Her throat contracted and the tears ran down her cheeks. The sea, in shades of green and amethyst, spread out before her like a piece of silk unrolled. It was perfectly calm, yet that wide gulf which separated her from Antony was full of terror for her. She turned to Charmian:

"What does life hold for me now? He who meant all my happiness has gone. Without his loving glance, the sound of his merry laughter, I shall have no joy in living."

The ideal confidante is one who makes her friend's grief her own. Although Charmian had deplored her mistress's relations with Antony and had felt, from the outset, that he would bring only misery to her beloved lady, yet she now feigned deep sorrow.

"The Triumvir's absence will make the Bruchium

seem an empty palace, but he will not tarry long away from you, my Queen. Even as he stepped on board the ship I heard him promise to return before the year is ended."

Cleopatra did not doubt his prompt return, for hope filled her veins, as the sap runs strong in the young tree in full leaf. But summer had barely begun, the days would drag along very slowly. Thus talking, under the protecting shade of ivory-handled fans held over them by two negro slaves, they went back to the terrace. The Queen stopped every few steps, for there were memories of Antony at each turn. There was the rose-coloured ibis, one leg tucked out of sight, who, motionless and quite tame, was standing on the grass, apparently lost in thought. The aromatic perfume of the carnations made her sigh, remembering that each night Antony had plucked one in passing, touched it to his lips, and put it in her bosom, saying: "I give you all my heart." And when he was not near to embrace her she always felt the warm fragrance of the flower as she breathed, like lips pressing against her breast. Nothing is more cruel in the absence of a loved one than the constant reminders of shared joys.

"Antony, come back to me, my beloved!" she cried in a sudden spasm of loneliness.

"You care too much, Madame. No living man is worthy of such love."

"It is easy to see, Charmian, that nothing has troubled the calm waters of your soul! Do you imagine that love is measured by the worthiness of the beloved? If that were true I could have loved no one so much as Cæsar; yet, as you know, Antony is the only one who has filled my whole soul."

She approached the fountain, where the water ran like living crystal and broke into foam at the basin's edge. The falling water brought the thought of the flying time that was taking away her happiness. Would those blissful days ever come again, or were they, like yesterday's flow of water, lost for ever?

Anxious to divert her from things which by their very charm were depressing, Charmian said gently:

"Will you not come now and try to sleep, Madame? To-morrow surely will bring you fresh courage."

Cleopatra had her royal robes laid aside, swallowed a draught of nepenthes to induce slumber, and said, as she closed her eyes:

"If I could only sleep on until he comes again!"

Life had to go on, however; four, five, six months, or more, would pass before Antony's return and Cleopatra was not the woman to give herself up to idle lamentations. Leaving the mourning veil and ashes to Dido of old, she resumed her sumptuous life and the royal routine of her daily duties.

Many things which had been neglected during those months of infatuation with her lover now claimed her attention. She took note of all the buildings, ships, and gardens in need of repair and saw that they were thoroughly overhauled and set in order. Her ministers were astonished to see how altogether conversant she was with the problems of state, and those who had thought her given over to frivolity were amazed with the way she handled the finances of the Government. She was equally proficient in reorganizing the army after the model of the legions which Antony had left with her; in adding to the marine service and in improving the administration generally.

As reigning sovereign, she set to work to improve the condition of her people; guarded against famine by irrigating the lands with fertilizing floods from the Nile; drove off the Nabathæan tribes who were threatening the Arabian frontier, showing that the ruler of Egypt, woman though she was, was the equal of the great kings of the world.

Like all her ancestors she had a love for building. She went from city to city with a host of architects, engineers, and artists, to see that the old temples were kept in proper repair. Those at Edfu, Hermonthis, and Coptis were rebuilt under her direction. The one at Dendera, which she enlarged, still shows her portrait carved on its tablets. She restored the Library at Alexandria and began the Cæsarium, whose excavated ruins reveal her admiration for Greek art. The last of the obelisks was erected during her reign: that Cleopatra's Needle, which, two thousand years later, was transported to the borders of the Thames, and now mournfully lifts its once rosy sides to the sooty skies of the British metropolis.

All these activities, however, could not make Cleopatra forget the aching void in her heart. In the midst of ceremonials, festivals, travels, she was continually asking herself: "What has become of Antony? Where is he? Has he forgotten me?"

Separation between lovers is endurable only if there is a steady interchange of letters. When Antony first left Egypt a galley came from Brindisi every ten days bringing long letters. In the beginning these were infinitely tender, filled with the solicitous grief that showed his anxiety in his absence. They reëchoed every expression of devotion which Cleopatra's letters contained. "Waking and sleeping you are always with me. I seek your presence everywhere and I feel that you are near," he wrote repeatedly. He said that public affairs were going forward satisfactorily and announced that, in order to hasten his return, he intended to put these in Pollion's care, as he understood all the details concerning them, while he himself was going at once to Syria and Palestine to reëstablish the authority which his long absence had compromised.

Since he could not be with her, Cleopatra much preferred having her lover in Asia Minor. That was where they were to come together again, in that country so like her own in climate, customs, habits of dress and tastes. There he would be reminded of her at every turn, whereas in Italy everything was different. By one of those unfailing feminine instincts, she felt that in Rome some unlooked-for turn of events would bring her disaster. She had never seen Octavius, but the fact that he was Cæsar's heir made him the rival and enemy of her little Cæsarion. Anything that occurred in Italy aroused her suspicion, and she could only hope that Antony, easily led and trustful as he was, would never fail to be on his guard.

Cleopatra's various enterprises were interrupted,

for the time being, by the birth of twins, to whom she gave the somewhat pretentious names of Helios and Selene. It seemed the propitious moment to remind Antony of the projected marriage which they had planned together and which was essential for the future protection of these children.

He responded by joyous and elaborate felicitations, saying that he was eager to legitimatize his claim to fatherhood as soon as possible. In confirmation of this assurance his messenger brought the young mother a coffer of carved gold, containing two pearls of perfect shape and wonderful orient, with the written words: "My lips have covered these with kisses, as I should love to cover your beautiful breasts, which are moulded in their likeness."

Such demonstrations made Cleopatra very happy. She loved—she was loved. That was enough for the present, and the future stretched before her like a flaming torch.

Then Antony's letters began to come less frequently. But what of that? He had left the coast; he was in the interior of the country, absorbed in necessary military details which left him little leisure for writing. Besides, he was remote from cities and consequently not exposed to the temptations of town life; why should she have any fears?

Her confidence that all was well was confirmed by the arrival of a Roman galley, sent from Asia, about the middle of the autumn. It brought neither gifts nor the customary sealed roll which the Queen was in the habit of seeing in the messenger's hand long before he reached her side. This time a courier came, requesting an audience with her. Cleopatra's heart throbbed with hope and fear. Her eyes sought those of the man who had so recently looked on her lover.

"How long since you have seen the Imperator?" she demanded.

"Twenty days, Madame."

"Where was he then?"

"At Samosata, on the border of the Commagene."

Her eager questions followed each other breathlessly. "How did he look? Was he sad or gay? What did he say to you? What message has he sent to me?"

This courier, Menecratus, was a freedman who had Antony's confidence, and whom long association with the Imperator had trained in the art of making a pleasing impression. He had abundant tact and discretion, an ideal interpreter for his master. He gave the following account to the Queen:

"When I went to receive the Imperator's orders he was neither sad nor gay. His face was radiant with that divine energy which is seen in the visage of Mars. The country all around him showed the marks of war. There were chariots, mules, troops of soldiers, shields glittering in the sun. He was holding the bridle of his fierce charger, which he was about to mount, in one hand; the other was on the pommel of his saddle. 'By the sacred geese which fly over the Capitol,' he said, 'go and report what you have seen. Tell Cleopatra that Mark Antony goes forth to conquer new kingdoms that he will soon lay at her feet.' "

So once again Cleopatra was comforted. Her lover was fighting for her sake; he was preparing for their future. Victory was in his path, and soon he would come back to her, so crowned with glory, so powerful in his conquests, that nothing, no one, could prevent the fulfilment of their magnificent plans.

The winter mists, however, were now obscuring the sea; all navigation was suspended. For more than three months there had been no tidings from Antony. The faith of Cleopatra was woven of a tissue so fragile that constant renewing was needed to keep the fabric whole. She was overwhelmed by a melancholy dread of possible disaster. The final date of his return was approaching. If he were not there! As she had no actual reasons to explain this persistent silence she tormented herself with the most rueful theories. He was the victim of poisoned arrows, a fatal fall, shipwreck; all these filled her imagination with depressing visions. She could not bear to be alone for a moment. Either Iras or Charmian was required to be in constant attendance. She kept them under a perpetual fire of questions, as an outlet for her own fears.

"The end of the year is close at hand, my Charmian. Why have I no word of his return?"

"Without doubt, Madame, he is planning to give you a happy surprise." The beautiful young Athenian girl spent hours at the feet of her mistress, her violet eyes fixed upon the Queen's anxious face, trying to reassure her.

But as the weary days dragged on and no news

came, the ominous menace, that seemed to threaten her from afar, drew nearer and the Queen was more difficult to comfort. One day she caught at Iras's hand, as though a sudden fear had come to her: "Can he have ceased to care for me? Has he put another woman in my place?"

"But Madame, he has known Cleopatra, what other woman could he find to take your place?" replied the Persian girl.

These fancies, vague at first, were now becoming cruel certainties. Travellers from Rome reported that Antony had returned from Asia, made his peace with Octavius, and the price of that peace was also known!

The tragic scene in which Cleopatra learns of her lover's marriage; the tears and passion which Shakespeare describes in words that make his stage a living world, leave nothing more to be told. By the silence, that interminable silence, which surrounded her, the Queen at last comprehended that dire misfortune had come to her. Her attendants tried to keep the truth back. No one of them could muster courage to speak. Was the news so horrible? Her mind leaped to the most terrible thing of all: "Is he dead? Has death frozen the warmest heart that ever throbbed?"

"No, no, Madame," Charmian cried, "Antony is alive, he is well." The Queen breathed again, but the dreaded disaster rushed to her mind. He had deserted her, then. Her agonized eyes put the question that her lips could not frame. No one answered. Everyone turned away and Charmian stammered incoherently.

"Iras, tell me, what is it?"

"There is nothing known definitely, Madame."

"But I insist on knowing definitely and at once," said Cleopatra, in a tone that suffered no denial.

The man who had brought the tidings was summoned. He proved to be a merchant, in Alexandria on his own business. He had gossiped, as all travellers do, bringing news from one town to the next. He was puzzled at being called to the palace.

"What is this tale? Speak out," commanded the Queen. Her look was terrifying. But the man had no sense of responsibility in repeating a story which was the subject of general discussion in Rome.

"Antony is married?" On hearing of this wedding with Octavia, which had been celebrated with the utmost pomp and magnificence, Cleopatra was beside herself with rage. Her pride, her dignity, her position, were as nothing. She was practically delirious with fury. She looked wildly around for someone on whom to wreak her vengeance. Those who were nearest to her shrank back in terror. It was the unfortunate wretch, whose only crime had been to bear ill-tidings, on whom her wrath fell. He was cursed, beaten, threatened with death. It was the natural outburst of her passionate nature, accustomed to command all, and who, for the first time, was confronted by overpowering misfortune and injury.

Was there no refuge from her torment? Could not the laws of the universe be altered? The first moments were horrible; a burst of tears followed her access of rage and she fainted. The servants fled, filling the whole palace with wailings. The doctors pressed forward, as though to aid someone in mortal need. Charmian was at her side.

"For the love of the gods, Madame, do not give your enemies the joy of seeing you crushed by this sorrow. Do not let them know how this blow has pierced your heart!"

"My Queen, my Queen, be brave!" whispered Iras, holding a handkerchief with some drops of stimulant to Cleopatra's lips. Gradually she grew calmer; she regained her self-control, but the wild frenzy was succeeded by a stupor. She felt as though a bottomless abyss had opened suddenly at her feet. "How can this be?" she murmured dully. "I trusted him and he told me that I meant all the world to him!" Her thoughts turned to the woman who had stolen her happiness. That sister of Octavius, Octavia—what kind of creature was she? The fierce desire to know the whole truth, in all its bitter details, surged in her breast, with the same violence that had caused her to pour out the stream of threats and curses so short a while before.

But the traveller was nowhere to be seen. Taking advantage of the confusion that followed the Queen's fainting fit he had fled. A diligent search revealed him, hidden in the hold of a ship. He had taken refuge there, deciding to give up the affairs that had brought him to Alexandria and, thankful to escape with his life, was hoping to get away on the ship without being detected.

He was terrified at being caught and it took repeated assurances that he would not be further punished to induce him to speak again. Fear had taught him discretion; he had learned that when speaking to the great and mighty it was wise to say only what they desired to hear. The plain truth was a crime. He showed the manners of a practised courtier when he had his second audience with Cleopatra.

The Queen, too, had undergone a great change. A sad, compelling curiosity dominated all other feelings. She was like a wanderer, lost in a dark wood, who seeks only light.

"Tell me something about Octavia," she said, with a gentleness that veiled the autocratic command. "You have seen her and know whether she is beautiful. Has she a wonderful expression? Is she dark or fair? What is the colour of her hair?" But however adroitly her questions might be put, this man, in whose ears her curses still rang, who was yet bruised from her shower of blows, would give no direct reply. According to him Octavia was a fright. Her eyes were dull, her hair scanty and fastened with austere, ash-coloured fillets.

"How old is she?" queried Cleopatra, still in the depths of despair, for however fascinating a deserted mistress may be, in her eyes the new love, though in reality a scarecrow, has all the attractiveness of a pure maiden whose unsullied youth is like to a fragrant garden in which her lover, or her husband, may wander at will to gather the flowers of happiness.

The merchant's tale was comforting, however. On hearing that Octavia was a widow, with two children; that she was without beauty and devoid of charm, with no power to kindle passion in a man's heart, Cleopatra had a moment of relief. Her anger had not died out, nor her bitter rancour against the lover who had deceived and betrayed her; she was, however, beginning to understand that this marriage had merely been a matter of political stratagem, a means of accomplishing Antony's designs.

In spite of this conviction, her fits of depression during the first few weeks after the news had come to her were so terrible that at times she felt that she must give up the struggle. She had always thought herself immune from jealousy, because of her conscious superiority over all other women. Now, little by little, it was eating into her heart. How could she be sure that Octavia was really a fright? that she had no power to charm? Was it true that her thick-set body had no attraction for Antony? After all, she had nothing to depend on but the word of a common man in the street. She recalled the affection that Antony had had for the hideous Fulvia; why should he not care for this new wife who was at least amiable and virtuous? Day by day this poison was entering into her soul.

At last she was so tortured by this canker of jealousy that she determined to put it away from her. By stupendous effort she tried to make herself believe that her love for Antony was dead, that she had never really cared for him and that consequently his marriage was a matter of indifference to her. In order to convince both herself and the world of this indifference she resumed her former life of dissipation with the young men of her court. Restrained no longer by those burning bonds that had kept her true to Antony, she went recklessly from one excess to another. Each involved a new degradation, each exhausted her by its gross intoxication, but nowhere could she find that oblivion for which her feverish heart longed. Crush, profane, trample on it, as she would, the memory of her cherished idol could not be rooted out. With inexhaustible persistence it pursued her; even in the warm embrace of her most ardent adorers, it came to make her shiver with horror at her own disloyalty to her lover. Wherever she went his dear image would appear suddenly before her, would cover her with his reproachful glance, as though he asked: "Why are you acting as though all were over between us? In spite of this seeming separation we are bound together in spirit for all eternity. Like ships, scattered for a time by the tempest, we shall surely come together again."

Her eyes smarted with tears as she invented excuses for her faithless lover. Surely he had been forced into this marriage for political reasons and against his will. Who had gained by this trap save Octavius? Who else would profit by this unholy alliance? This scheme had been devised by that cunning fellow that he might make his sister a sentinel to watch over Antony and report his doings to his colleague. The brute! Half vexed, half tenderly, she would again invoke the loved image, addressing him in imagination: "How guileless you were! You who had every right to rule, who could have chosen your mate and controlled the world—why should you play such a petty part, be made to obey like a little child? Oh! the pity of it!"

And then a ray of hope gleamed. That same

weakness which had taken her lover away from her arms might be used to restore him to her. Her kisses were indelibly printed on his forehead; why should she not re-kindle that fire which was probably still smouldering? And in one of those ecstasies, which were like a torch touched by a passing spark, she cried aloud: "I will tempt him back again! The hour is not far off when I shall carry him away from Rome, from his wife, from Octavius, from all who have thought that they were stronger than I."

She did not trust simply to that thread, which, like a new Ariadne, she had put in her Theseus's hands. She put all her resources to work to carry out her purpose. Octavius had his spies; she would have hers. These she despatched immediately, with orders to keep close watch over Antony; to learn the innermost secrets of his household; to leave no stone unturned to discover all that was going on there.

The first accounts sent back by these agents brought her only added distress. Apparently the newly wedded couple were happy and living in perfect harmony. She declined to be discouraged by these reports, however. "If I exhaust all the men in my kingdom," she said, "I will place spies in every corner and in time they will surely find the crack in his armour!"

When she first heard of the disagreements between the brothers-in-law, especially of the silly quarrel over the cock-fight, she was delighted. At last she had found the long-looked-for crack, and that would destroy the whole household, make it fall in ruins. She knew Antony too well to believe that he would tolerate a rival for any length of time. Her chief object now was to entice him away from Rome. With untiring diligence she organized a secret society composed of courtesans, freedmen, and court attendants. She instructed these to call Antony's attention to certain familiar things sent from the Bruchium; to the fragrance of perfumes associated with his days spent there with her; by a word spoken at the right moment to set him dreaming of those months in Egypt. The dealers in oracles also had their mission. They were to encourage the Triumvir to consult them, and, as though all Nature were speaking through them with one voice, they were told to repeat the famous words of his horoscope: "The star of your fortune is at its zenith, but the star of Octavius seeks to eclipse it. Your glory fears his glory, your power will diminish when the two stars come together."

Other influences were also working in unison with Cleopatra. If certain of his friends, like Ahenobarbus and Pollion, had urged Antony's marriage with Octavia and had jeered at this man of valour being subject to the yoke of Egypt's queen, others, more far-sighted, divined that some day she would regain her sovereignty over him. Among these latter was Quintus Dellius, he who had arranged the affair at Tarsus. He understood this passionate woman better than any one else and knew that she was capable of any deed to gain possession of her lover. There was also Fonteius Capito, a subtle observer of human nature, who had written before Antony had been wedded a year: "Yes, Antony's marriage is apparently a happy one, but that he is beginning to be bored by it is evident to every one." These two men thought it wise to forestall future developments and they kept up a close correspondence with the Queen, keeping her in touch with everything that could be of interest to her. She was not only informed of the most intimate details of Antony's household, but of all the governmental complications against which the Triumvir had to fight. The increasing boldness of the Parthian invasions, the coast pillage of the pirates of Sextus Pompey, the uprisings of the poorer classes, their refusals to pay the taxes. All these disturbances in Roman territory gave her fresh reasons for hope. The day she heard that Antony was leaving his wife to her maternal duties and sailing for Athens, she was overcome with joy.

The game was not yet won, but at least she was no longer tormented by visions of Octavia happy in the arms of her husband. Those two were separated and Antony's wife, desolate in her loneliness, would now suffer as she had done. If Cleopatra were not entirely comforted by this knowledge, it at any rate helped her to bear her own trials more patiently!

Stirred by alternate emotions, she sometimes felt as though all were lost; then again she exulted in the thought that her sorrows were almost over. The most cruel moment was when she heard of the reconciliation at Tarentum. She had been following with intense interest all the details of the fray and its results, and was planning to gather up the fragments of these broken alliances and construct a new power therefrom, and now this disappointment had come. It was a severe lesson and would have discouraged any one made of less stern stuff than this indomitable woman. She had, however, a gift of clairvoyance which could not be deceived for any length of time. Although the treaty to renew peace between the brothers-in-law was formally drawn up, although it was sealed with offerings to the gods, libations, and festivals, and, more important still, by betrothals of offspring which doubled and trebled the many bonds between the families of Julius and Antony, it was very evident that this reconciliation would only be a temporary alliance.

Antony had fulfilled his part of the contract at once. A hundred brass-prowed triremes, twenty despatch boats, and as many lighter vessels, lying in the harbour at Tarentum, had already been given over to Octavius. And what had Octavius offered in exchange? Promises, nothing but promises. Sixteen legions and a quantity of war supplies had been agreed upon in the treaty, but as yet none of these had materialized. There was nothing to do but trust in the good faith of Octavius, and to those who knew him there seemed small chance of these promises being carried out.

But Antony was confident that they would be. His own loyalty made him often the dupe of other people. At this time he was especially trustful, for he had Octavia as an intermediary and there could be no possible doubt as to her sincerity. He had no misgivings on that score and, counting on the promised reinforcements being forthcoming when required, he gave himself up to his own ambitious plans and left Italy for Antioch.

His wife went with him as far as Corcyra, proud of having been able to serve him, and more tenderly devoted to him than ever. There they parted, he to go on with his preparations for his coming campaign, she to return to Rome and see that the conditions of the treaty were carried out as promptly as possible.

Antony's first object was to procure money. Since the Imperators had persistently ravaged the cities and country, violated the temples and overtaxed the people, this necessary commodity of war had grown very scarce. To extort it from Italy was impossible. Greece had been exploited to its utmost resources. The provinces of Asia still remained; rich always, as a result of the advanced, scientific agriculture which made the land yield abundantly. But the land owners had been exasperated by toiling for Roman profit and there was a general effort to evade the taxes by violence and fraud. Many of these offenders had been executed for opposing the law, and these conditions had brought about disastrous results.

Antony found himself greatly embarrassed. To declare that it was his need of money alone that prompted him to return to Cleopatra would be to ignore the complexities of human nature. It is true that in those trying hours when the censors returned empty-handed, with accounts of money due, his thoughts naturally reverted to the overflowing treasury of the Egyptian Queen, with those accumulated riches buried in caverns beneath the earth. If he had not deserted Cleopatra this untold wealth would have been at his command. He could have employed it to sustain that army, which was, he firmly believed, to give him the empire of the world.

But why waste time in dreaming of that vanished opportunity which would come to him no more? Yet his mind went back again and again to those days spent in the palace of the Bruchium. He saw his enchanting hostess, with her dark, flashing eyes, her mocking smile, her golden-tinted flesh—that golden colour which made his blood hot at the mere thought of it. What was the mysterious magic of this woman that the very idea of her brought the sweat to his brow and stirred his innermost being, even after these years of separation? All the time he had been in Rome he had seen her in visions; embraced her in his dreams. Even when in Octavia's arms he had been ever conscious of the mistress whom he had deserted, and her phantom form would slip into the place of the actual woman by his side. These hallucinations had disturbed him. As a faithful husband he had tried to thrust them away from him. To-day, in this land of perfumed luxury that brought back the days he had spent at Tarsus, they had complete mastery over him. His blood ran faster; he was defenceless against these persistent memories of his mistress. He saw her in every possible posture; the cat-like grace of her movements; the exquisite colour and lines of her draperies. He heard the soft harmony of her voice, and all these images told him that he was powerless to withstand her spell.

But would the mere personal possession of her have satisfied him? Would it have sufficed in place of the social triumphs, interests, and ambitions that bound the Triumvir to Roman life? He was not certain as to this, but complications arose which freed him from further doubts and scruples.

The promised reënforcements from Octavius had not come and there were certain wise men who predicted that they never would come. These troubles increased the discontent that was fermenting in him. He not only nursed a fierce hatred against his treacherous colleague, whose delay was endangering all his projects, but he had a growing prejudice against everyone connected with him. Even Octavia, invaluable and faithful as she had been, did not escape his suspicion. It was unpardonable that she should be the sister of the most perfidious of men. Besides, at this great distance she was powerless to help him. If absence be a mirage which gives greater radiance to some images, it dims others, and often makes the more delicate ones vanish, as though they were swallowed up in mist. Each day was gradually effacing the gracious contour of his wife from Antony's mind, while the voluptuous outlines of his mistress grew clearer and more irresistible.

Fonteius Capito, who understood his master's anxiety, struck the decisive blow. Antony had just experienced a fresh disappointment in seeing promised confiscations for Peloponnesus reduced to a fourth of the original amount agreed upon. When Fonteius suggested that Cleopatra would be only too glad to lend any money that he needed, Antony staggered, as though he had received a sudden blow.

"How do you know that?" he asked impatiently.

"She has requested me to tell you so."

Was it possible that she was still thinking of him? That after all he had done she bore him no ill will? He must be dreaming! He stared at Capito, fearing he might deny the words that he had just spoken. But no; explanations followed and Antony was assured that Cleopatra had never ceased to love him, that she was still eager for his success.

What miracle of love was this, that after being stabbed, scorned, trodden under foot and profaned, thus came to life, or rather showed that it had never ceased to live! In a second Antony's exhausted energy was renewed. It was the ecstatic joy of an invalid recovering from a protracted illness, of a convalescent who takes life up again, to find it more beautiful than he had ever realized.

On being despatched to Alexandria, Capito had no occasion to copy the diplomacy of Dellius in order to induce Cleopatra to follow him. She was more than ready to go. Her days of coquetry were over. She now only desired to join her lover, to be assured that she could hold him, and to begin immediately that contest with her rival in which the more persistent and less scrupulous combatant was certain of the victory.

Some letters from Antony had made his situation and its difficulties quite clear to her. He was on the eve of a campaign, without money, without the necessary troops. Outside aid was essential. She would supply this assistance; be the beneficent goddess, who at the crucial moment turns the wheel of Fortune.

Ships were loaded at once; some with gold, others bearing beasts of burden; others again laden with machinery and abundant supplies of wheat; all the necessary stores to sustain the strength of the army. When these were packed to the netting, the purple sails of the royal galley were unfurled. The negro rowers grasped their silver-mounted oars, and, over gracious waves that seemed to make way for her tranquil passage, Antony's mistress sped to her lover.

It was at Antioch again that Antony awaited Cleopatra; the same Antioch where, five years before, he had begun to dream of her beneath the cedars and the palm trees. In the evening, under the glowing sunset skies, she stood erect, beside the silken canopy, looking as though she wished to hasten the flying ship to reach him sooner. His heart throbbed; his eyes grew dim; the blood surged in his ears. It seemed that the whole sea was beating against his breast. Amidst shoutings and acclamations he conducted the fair traveller to the old palace of the Seleucides that he had prepared for her with a luxury that rivalled the splendours of the Bruchium.

Alone at last, they looked at each other in silence. So many months had passed, so many things had happened since their parting that they seemed scarcely able to recognize each other. Was this the son of Bacchus, with such a troubled brow? Cleopatra, young as she was, and more beautiful than ever, bore the marks of suffering. Though her passionate mouth had the vivid red of an open pomegranate, a curve of bitterness had changed its expression. She had lost the serene look of former days. In the storm of life she had been bruised against the rocks of fate. Her heart, her royal heart, whose only dream had been to conquer, had known the humiliation of longing and of tears. At this moment, on the verge of victory, she was torn by conflicting emotions. Even as she yielded to his irresistible fascination she had the agonized thought: "Why do I still love this man who has put another woman in my place?"

"What are you thinking about?" demanded Antony, almost brutally, as though he dreaded her reply.

"I am thinking that you are no longer mine; that you never really loved me," she answered bitterly.

"Do not say such things!"

But her mind was made up. If only to show her generosity in forgiving him, she would let him see how guilty he had been.

"If you had really cared, how could you have had the heart to desert me?—to betray me, after all your promises?—to leave me, as you did, sorrowful, humiliated, and alone?"

Antony knelt before her, a penitent, overwhelmed with grief. He tried to prove his innocence. "I love you; I have always loved you and you only. Never, for one instant, have I loosed the bond that unites us." Cleopatra listened, but an ironical smile was on her lips.

"How can you understand my difficulties? The political necessity which has controlled all my actions? You have no idea what I have suffered."

But she would not be convinced. "If you had

really loved me——" Antony stopped her. He leaped to his feet like a young Hercules, threw his arms around her, and pressed his quivering lips to her own.

"Forgive me! Only say that you forgive me!" he pleaded.

She was beginning to yield but turned away, with a last effort to make him believe that she was impervious to his prayers.

"Miserable creature that I am! Never have I so longed to hold you in my arms as I do at this moment, when I feel that you have every right to hate me, to curse me!"

She was looking at him through her dark lashes. A slight twitching at her throat showed the emotion that made them both the helpless victims of an overmastering passion.

"I have cursed you, yes; but hated you, how could I?"

They clasped each other, fiercely, passionately, as though to crush out all remembrance of what had come between them. In that moment they both forgot the cowardice, the bitterness; all that did not make for happiness, for the ecstasy of being together, was wiped out. The old passionate ardour, their very breath of life, without which they could only languish and die, had come back, nothing else mattered. Their separation was only a vast emptiness. Once more they were in that enchanted garden where Fate had first brought them together. They were wandering in its secret paths and would abide there for ever.

Whatever might happen afterward these infatuated lovers, with no interest, no desire except for each other, would wander hand in hand through fields of triumph and adversity, conquerors even to the end, since they would fix the hour for leaving life and would go down to immortality together.

Antony had ample cause for self-reproach. Haunted by the many wrongs done his mistress, he now became her slave, and was absorbed in carrying out her slightest wish. There was never a more extravagantly generous lover! Cleopatra was interested in literature; he sent two hundred thousand rolls of papyrus stolen from Pergamus, for the library she had just rebuilt. She had a passion for art; several sanctuaries were rifled and their treasures transported to Alexandria.

It was as easy for him to offer her kingdoms as it was for other men to cover their mistresses with jewels, or to lay fortunes at their feet. Invested with sovereign power, he gave away the Roman provinces as casually as though they had formed part of his own patrimony. In addition to Phœnicia, which he had presented to her in payment of the famous wager over the pearls, the kingdoms of Cilicia, Chalcides, and part of Arabia were annexed to Egypt. The Queen also coveted Judea, land of palms and spices, with its capital, Jerusalem, into which poured the gold procured by the Jews from the four quarters of the world; but it was difficult to dethrone Herod, the King, who had reconquered it after a hard struggle. Antony conceded the crown to this ally, who was to be of use to him, on condition that Cleopatra should receive the revenue from its most bountiful districts, as well as the palms from Samaria, and the roses of Jericho, which were cultivated for her only.

Some of the graver members of Antony's circle, among them Ahenobarbus (who never hesitated to express openly what others were whispering), resented this free use of Roman property. But, drunk alike with pride and passion, Antony replied: "Short-sighted men that you are, can you not understand that the true grandeur of Rome is shown less in her conquests and the extent of her possessions than in the generosity which her riches makes possible?"

Nor was it bad policy to strengthen and enrich the woman who aspired to be, not only his ally, but his wife! For Cleopatra had never renounced her original plan. Having gathered wisdom from experience, tired of joys which eluded her, of crowns which often melted away, she was determined to carry out this project without further delay.

At this moment, when Antony was making ready to draw on her treasures it was only fair that she should share the benefits. In the same way that she would help him to conquer Persia, thus making him more powerful than all other rulers, she would play the part of his companion, by fair means or foul, be present the day that he would ride in triumph to the Capitol.

An arrangement so entirely in accord with her own interests has caused Cleopatra to be considered a cold, calculating woman, who weighed and planned everything for her own glory, and used Antony merely as an easy instrument in her hands. To deny that she had schemes, and that, convinced of the Triumvir's weakness, she had made up her mind to rule for him and to direct his actions to her own advantage, would be to close one's eyes to actual evidence. But when have love and self-interest been proved irreconcilable? Did her dream of becoming a world-sovereign in any way lessen her passion? To marry Antony, to unite her lot with a passionate lover as well as a powerful ruler, to bind him so that he could never again escape from her, that was the dream of this far-seeing, level-headed woman.

There were serious obstacles to be considered, however, the chief one being Antony's marriage with Octavia. Divorces, to be sure, were neither rare nor difficult in Rome. Originally, in a society founded on religious faith and respect for the home, adultery had been the necessary cause; but at that time they were granted for less serious reasons. Incompatibility of temper, provided it was not proved by both sides, was accepted as a common cause of divorce. At one time, so lax were the morals, a man could put away the mother of his children simply on the ground that she no longer pleased him, that he preferred someone else.

But how could such injustice be done to a woman whose birth and rank had placed her near Olympus? What a brutal wrong against the pure, the revered sister of Octavius! Nor was this all. An ancient law, inscribed on the "Twelve Tables," prohibited all marriages between Roman rulers and foreigners. This law had always been rigorously enforced, and disastrous results would have followed its transgression by the first citizen of the Republic. Antony tried to persuade his audacious mistress of the danger that this cruel and unreasonable act would involve. He showed her how the common people, always ready to throw down their idols, would take sides with Octavius, how the Senate, indignant at his conduct, would rise up in arms.

But Cleopatra was obstinate. She determined to have her revenge on Antony and she reminded him of Cæsar.

"He was married to Calpurnia, he faced the same obstacles that seem insurmountable to you, yet he did not hesitate to divide with me the flourcake used to consecrate espousals, and to declare me before all the world as his lawful wife!"

"That was on his return from Persia," interrupted Antony. "When the voice of victory is loud enough to stifle all recriminations, I will do the same. Wait until I have conquered. . . ."

But Cleopatra had had the cruel experience of what happens during separations; she would wait no longer. Their marriage should be the express condition of that pardon that she had granted in the excitement of those first moments of meeting, but which each succeeding day she was more inclined to withdraw. Crises of jealousy, continual reproaches, bitter railings on the subject of the lawful wife, perpetually reminded Antony of his sins and the need of making atonement.

The man who had been brought up in Fulvia's school knew only too well what punishment women can inflict. These scratches of the beautiful tigress, far from cooling his passion, fanned it into flame. He felt bound to her for life. Her gift of intensifying life, of making it feverishly exciting, her ferocious caresses, her pretended threats of breaking off all relations, her swoons, all this exhilaration which formed part of their daily life, how could he leave it to go back to the tameness of an honest affection, and take up the routine of married life? He would have to do as Cleopatra demanded. Their marriage should be celebrated in the first days of spring, before the army began the new campaign.

On hearing of this outrageous plot, the Triumvir's friends were beside themselves with indignation. If Dellius, Capito, and Plancus, who lived chiefly by his favours, kept silence for fear of displeasing him, others, who were more independent, did not hesitate to express their opinions. The proposed marriage would be a revolutionary act, an unprecedented scandal which might well upset the whole Roman Government. Public opinion would be unanimous against this contempt for the oldest traditions. The Patricians would take the insult as a personal offence and would defend Octavia's cause; and as to Octavius, his fury over this affront to his sister would pass all bounds, and who could foresee the consequences?

Antony, fully aware of the justice of these warnings, hesitated, tried to gain time. Whatever way he turned storms came down on him. By alarming Cleopatra, showing her the danger of a scandal when one is not strong enough to carry it over the heads of the people, he gained her consent, for the moment at least, to a middle course. The marriage would be celebrated, as he had promised, the official act would be inscribed on the civil registers at Antioch, as well as in Alexandria, but, until the termination of the war, there would be no official notification made to the Roman Senate. In this way, while he became the husband of the rich Egyptian, he would still remain the husband of the woman whom, by lawful marriage, he had wedded according to the rites of the Latin monogamy.

There was no justice in this, no consistency. It was not possible that the same man could bear the title of King of Egypt and of Imperator at the same time; that a Proconsul could arrogate to himself, as a satrap, the right to have more than one wife at any one time.

But Cleopatra's lover had, for the time being, lost his senses. The good fortune which had followed him from his early youth, his habitual laxness of morals, made him accept the absurd, confound folly with reason. Not knowing which to choose he pretended to need all his titles. It was certainly not the moment to renounce the most important thing of all, the right to appear before his allies with the authority of Triumvir. He had neither the courage to decline the royal hand which was held out to him filled with love and treasure, nor to put away that other little hand which held his honour as a Roman.

Intoxicated with his triumphs, having had no reverses to teach him moderation, his violent nature demanded life in its highest key. He would not be bound by any restriction. The whole world seemed to lie before him like a huge field whose entire harvest was his by right.

To the kingdoms he had already given Cleopatra he added Crete, as a wedding gift, with its forests of maple and satinwood, of sandal and ebony; with its luxuriant larches whose branches swept the ground while waiting for the trunks to grow thick enough to furnish masts for the ships in the harbour.

Although fully aware of their value, these splendid donations were not enough for Cleopatra. Goddess as she was, her worship demanded sacrifices. What she was about to exact should be the price that Antony would be forced to pay for Egypt's gold. As he had not consented to divorce Octavia, he must at least promise that he would never see her again.

"The man who desires peace in his household has no regard for promises," says an ancient proverb. Diverted for the moment from Rome as Antony was, entranced by the fascinations of the Orient, of what importance was the guardian of his penates? She whom he believed wholly absorbed in the care of his children?

Antony was mistaken. He was an indifferent psychologist, and under the modest demeanour of the noble woman, whom the Athenians had compared to their Pallas, he had never divined her passionate soul; in the faithful and devoted wife he had not recognized the *woman,* hungry for her share of happiness.

In reality, since their parting at Corcyra, Octavia's only thought had been for her husband. She could not give him daily proofs of her love, but she could help him. And she began to gather together money, provisions, army equipments, all the things that a general requires for a campaign. Although she had been unable to make Octavius fulfil his promises, she had in spite of his opposition, recruited two thousand picked men, supplied them with the necessary funds, and, happy in the thought that these fearless and splendidly equipped volunteers would form an invincible cohort for the Imperator, she had engaged ships and embarked with them for Greece.

When he heard with what a valuable cargo Octavia was arriving at Piræus, Antony was greatly perplexed. He was not wholly hardened in evil-doing. Weakness was his chief fault. He acted on impulse and, with the thoughtlessness of a child, turned his back on the consequences. The present was all-important, the future did not count. When he married Cleopatra and promised never again to see Octavia, he had reckoned on the soothing effect of time and distance, and also on that nameless assistance from the gods who never yet had failed him. And now he suddenly faced a definite situation, a two-horned dilemma which led to equally disagreeable results. It would be madness to refuse the valuable help which Octavia was bringing him; yet to accept her generous gift without according her a welcome, without rewarding this god-sent messenger with even a kiss, made him hot with shame. But what was he to do? There was Cleopatra, fascinating and headstrong, jealous of her rights and not willing to yield an inch. In imagination he heard her bitter reproaches and was distracted by their accusing tone. What did his promises mean? The last were not the least binding, and they were strengthened by a soft arm around his neck, a honey-sweet mouth near his own, and eyes, now full of infinite tenderness, now threatening a storm more terrifying to a lover than the blaze of lightning and the roar of thunder.

But the image of Octavia had its influence too, and as she drew near it seemed as though her sweet soul had the same power that it had held for the past three years. There was no need for him to read again her last letter. The words were always ringing in his ears: "Why do you stay away? Have I offended you in any way? I thought it wise to come myself with the men and armaments that you asked me to get together. Am I wrong? I heard that you were about to start on your great campaign. May I embrace you before you go? At your bidding I will cross the seas that divide us, or if you do not want me to come I will await your return. As you know, I live only to serve you. But if you do not care for my aid and do not want me to wait for you, what will become of me?"

This tender, submissive devotion wrung his heart. He wanted to reply, not from love, for the brief passion that this pure Roman woman had roused in him was already dead, but—his conscience was not dead. His changes from sinner to penitent were a constant surprise to his contemporaries. They have recorded his grief at Fulvia's death, although during her life he had repaid her fierce devotion by gross ingratitude.

And now it was Octavia's turn to stir his heart

and conscience. With the wheedling tenderness which, whatever wrong they may have done them, men use toward women they love, he pleaded with Cleopatra:

"I shall be away from you only three days. What are three days when we have a lifetime of love before us?"

But he could not escape from her suspicious eyes. She had suffered too keenly ever again to feel free from distrust. Why should the sorrow and tears of this woman whom she had never seen concern her? No, she would make no concessions. Antony should never again seen Octavia.

The preparations for war went on. Antioch was like a vast parade-ground. The cohorts passed through the gate of Daphne every day. They marched with fearless step, making the paved street ring under their buskins. A brilliant group of horsemen was seen in the midst of the glittering lances and eager young faces. Pell-mell with the Greeks came the Gauls, preceded by their standards. Then came the baggage: mules whose backs bent under the burden of stones and weapons; camels loaded like ships; chariots whose noise resounded through the silent old streets; and troop after troop marched by, each raising dust in its turn. Antony was about to leave for those Mesopotamian plains that stretched out in the distance against the misty blue horizon.

The thought of this new separation, which was bound to be long and beset with dangers—for the Parthians were the most treacherous of enemies—disturbed Cleopatra greatly. The memory of the brief, happy nights, the delicious days together, was only an additional grief; and she had one tormenting thought: Surely Antony had not broken his promise; he had not crossed the inlet of the sea which separated him from Greece? But Octavia was there, always there, expecting him, waiting for him, probably sending messages to him, and of late he had been preoccupied. In spite of his slavish devotion to her, Cleopatra was in continual dread of his secret escape to her rival, were it only for an hour. Before returning to Egypt she was determined to have Octavia go back to Rome. Once there, she would have at least the bitter satisfaction of feeling that her hated rival was at the greater distance from the husband who belonged to them in common.

As Antony was going to camp one morning to review his troops, he noticed that she looked unusually gloomy.

"You are depressed; what is troubling you?" he asked tenderly.

"You know very well why I am miserable. I cannot endure having Octavia so near us," she answered, frowning.

He tried to seem indifferent. "Why should she disturb you, since we never see her?"

"She has come here to defy me."

Making no attempt at a defence which he knew would be futile, he said:

"The poor woman!" and went out to join his escort, whose horses were pawing with impatience under the palace windows.

With that acute faculty, peculiar to people of

passionate temperament, for making themselves miserable when a desire is not immediately fulfilled, Cleopatra imagined Antony as deceptive, evasive, ready to betray her for the second time. The very exclamation that he had uttered on leaving her—"the poor woman!"—rang in her ears and increased her anger. What tender pity he had put into the words! How plainly he had implied that she was innocent of any offence! Did he still love her? After all, it was quite possible that this intriguing woman had retained her influence over his weak heart. At all events they were still good friends, and that alone was a torment to the woman who, for her own advantage, would have been willing to destroy the world. She would have no peace until Octavia went away, and she resolved to secure her banishment that very day.

In the evening, when the Imperator returned, with the confident air of a man who, having satisfactorily accomplished his day's work, expects a certain reward, he had the disagreeable surprise of a cold welcome. Cleopatra had decided to smile upon him only on condition that he would carry out her wishes at once. She began:

"You are sacrificing our happiness for the sake of a woman who no longer means anything to you!"

"She is certainly nothing to me that can distress you, since I love only you!"

"But you are still good friends!"

He had gone over the same subject so often, defending himself and pointing out the motives for his attitude, that the futility of further words was clear to him.

"How you do hate her!" he exclaimed, in a tone which implied, "How unjust you are!"

This reproach was the last touch. Cleopatra was exasperated, and in a fury, demanded:

"And you! How can you pretend that you no longer love her?"

Kisses are the only sure means of persuasion between lovers, and she refused to let him come near her. Worn out, disheartened, like a man who has lost all interest in life, Antony asked sadly:

"What is it that you wish? What further proof do you require from me?"

A papyrus leaf was lying ready on the table.

"Write!" commanded his despot. "Send an order to Octavia to depart for Rome as quickly as possible!"

This ungracious act was repugnant to Antony's instinctive gallantry. He had never treated any woman rudely. Should he behave like a blackguard to the one who had every right to expect from him the greatest gratitude and consideration? He hesitated, his hand resting on his knee.

"Yet you pretend to love me!" she murmured, her breath fanning his cheek.

He realized that if he refused he would never again feel that sweet breath mingling with his own; that he would have to leave her, go to distant lands, contend with opposing forces, without having that last embrace which inspires men with courage and on the eve of battle makes them confident of victory. Without this powerful stimulus nothing seemed worth struggling for, his mighty enterprise would be in vain.

With a sudden movement Cleopatra slipped the stylet between his fingers.

"Write, write," she cried.

Slowly, painfully, as though the words were loath to come, he wrote the letter.

"Now sign it!"

He put his name at the bottom of the written lines. Everything had been prepared. The papyrus was rolled closely around the stick. When the seal was pressed on the wax it seemed to shrink like bleeding flesh. An officer came in for instructions. The message was handed him with orders to deliver it at once to Octavia. An instant later they heard him galloping in the direction of Seleucia. There he would find a boat which, in a few hours, would bring him to Piræus.

Not knowing the reason for Antony's prolonged silence, Octavia was counting the days. It was nearly a month since she had arrived at Piræus and she was still waiting for a reply to her letters. Rumours were afloat which might have given her a suggestion of the truth. She knew that the Queen of Egypt had landed in Asia; that this whimsical woman had put hordes of gold at the Imperator's disposal. There was a report of a political alliance between them. There were even whispers of a secret marriage. But to Octavia's virtuous and upright mind, totally unprepared for such tidings, the terrible truth was difficult to comprehend. To realize that such treachery was possible she required surer proof than mere hearsay.

The only proof that could convince her was already on its way: the affirmation signed by Antony.

Yet it did not tell her the whole truth. Under pretext of an unlooked-for change of plans he had written that he was obliged to leave Antioch sooner than he had expected, expressed formal regret at being prevented from coming to thank her for her assistance, and intimated his wish that she reëmbark as soon as possible and go back to Rome.

In reading this letter, with no word of affection, with nothing of her beloved husband in it but his signature, Octavia felt her heart grow cold. What had happened to him? Instantly her worst fears were confirmed. Her eyes were opened and she saw the heartless facts as they were; her husband no longer loved her. However opposed to deception she might be, she longed for the hour that had just passed, when she was at least ignorant of her misery. There was nothing to comfort her. She had to drink to the last drop the bitter cup of knowledge.

Two days later Octavia, always submissive to her husband's will, left Greece and turned toward Rome. Her tear-stained face was heavily veiled. The Athenians watched her set sail, saw her quit the beautiful city of song and play, where, as comrade of Dionysos, she had been crowned with myrtle. They looked after her as she took that lonely road which Hagar, Penelope, Ariadne, and many others had followed, and which to the end of time, the faithlessness of men will force on loyal women.

Cleopatra was triumphant. She had seized with both hands the reins of the chariot of victory. She was again madly in love with Antony, and, as always when she had made him yield to her wishes, she covered him with kisses. She wanted to stay with him, but it was imperative that she go back to Egypt. This new Jason was going to unexplored countries where he was confident of finding another golden fleece.

Cleopatra went with him as far as the frontier of the Euphrates—sometimes on horseback, galloping with the grace of the Queen of the Amazons, sometimes ensconced in a litter with clusters of ostrich feathers waving at the four corners and curtains fastened with crystal chains. Twelve Nubians bore this litter on their sturdy shoulders. When the wind blew two faces could be seen behind those soft silk curtains, two faces resting very near each other. In the evening a tent was pitched. With its golden roof, its walls draped with brilliant red, outlined by flaming torches, it looked like a huge bonfire blazing in the midst of the camp. Here the travellers, on the eve of separation, built their fond dreams. On their return—that return which was to be so soon—their marriage would be proclaimed. They would put on that double crown which their union would win for them. The world would belong to them; it would be their enchanted palace, a glorious, inexhaustible garden of delight. For with these lovers glory and love were always intermingled.

The morning that they were to part, with hands clasped they looked at each other in silence, as though each wished to imprint the vision of the other before it vanished.

"To-morrow my eyes will no longer behold you," sighed Cleopatra.

"Mine will see you always," said Antony, "for you will be nearer to me than the blaze of the sun by day, or the light of the stars at night."

In order to see him until the last moment Cleopatra climbed a hill which commanded the surrounding country. The rocks in the river made it a whirling torrent, foam-flecked and roaring furiously. When Antony had reached the farther side, he turned again, saluting Cleopatra for the last time, and described a wide circle with his flashing sword. Before him lay a deep valley. All was light, transparent green, touched with the gold of the coming harvest. The great shadow of Alexander seemed to point out the path for him to follow. Impetuously he threw himself on his horse, which leaped forward, his royal purple mantle floating in the wind.

VIII

The Two Rivals

IN SPITE of all the precautions for secrecy, Octavius soon learned what had happened at Antioch. His resentment was keen, for in addition to the insult to his sister, which reflected on himself, he could not accept calmly an alliance that added a crown to his colleague's glory. Would Antony, this lucky adventurer, succeed in his invasion of Parthia? To Greece, Egypt, and Asia Minor, his rightful share as one of the Triumvirate, would he annex Armenia as well? And Persia? All that fabulously rich Orient, on which Alexander had built his matchless fame?

Where would his power end? What pinnacle would he leave unscathed? A wave of hatred surged up in Octavius's heart. Knowing, however, that the hour had not yet come to unmask his real sentiments, he pretended to ignore the matrimonial complications of Octavia's treacherous husband. When he and Antony were together his attitude was friendly, ostentatiously fraternal. He even begged the gods to favour the expedition which he was hoping to see fail, and by pious libations he made every pretence of kindly feeling, hiding his personal grievances. He made the mistake, however, of criticizing his brother-in-law's habit of life.

This remonstrance, coming from a man whose recent marriage, preceded by adultery and rape, had scandalized all decent people, was naturally ridiculous. It brought a return thrust from Antony, which, though cynical, was not lacking in force and wit. "Of what are you accusing me?" he wrote from Alexandria, whither he had gone to visit Cleopatra, in the brief interval between two battles. "My relations with the Queen are not new. You know very well that I have been her lover for the past nine years! As for you! have you ever been faithful to one woman? I wager by the time that this letter reaches you your Livia will have had cause for complaint, and that you have already quarrelled with Tertulia, Terentella, or Rufilla, probably all three of them. If a man serves the gods and his country, what matter with whom he takes his pleasures?"

Antony was in no hurry to raise his mask of secrecy and announce his imitation marriage. He wanted to wait until after his second campaign into Persia—from which he looked for happier results than the first had given him—before risking the inevitable reproaches and disturbances that might involve more than the family relation. Clad in the armour of victory he would have nothing to fear. He therefore tore himself from the tender arms that held him and returned to the field of battle.

His troops, awaiting him on the Median frontier, accorded him, as always, an enthusiastic welcome. They were his old soldiers, who had often fought under his standards and were ready to follow wherever he led. They had implicit faith in him, understood the breadth of his ambitions, and were touched with the fire of his aspirations. They were confident that *his* fortune would be *their* fortune; that they would have, in their turn, quite as much glory and even more gold than the veterans of Cæsar had won.

Why should they not have believed in the success of their incomparable chief? Their hero, brave, alert, always on the spot when needed; a warlike genius, prompt in action, generous to a fault, never weary; who met good fortune and evil with the same indomitable smile!

This popularity was too precious for him to neglect any means of adding to it. Kindly always, he won hearts still more by his epicurean indulgences, which he allowed his subordinates to share with him. A lover of good living, he wanted happy faces around him. He confined his rigorous discipline to the time of action; in camp he authorized a freedom from restriction which was a new departure in the life of Roman soldiers. What a contrast between the old bands of Marius, valiant, it is true, but who marched under the lictor's whip, and the spontaneous zeal of Antony's troops, who were ready to suffer and to die for their leader! A striking instance of their devotion was shown in the reply made by his men in the passes of Armenia, where they were enduring the combined miseries of fatigue, hunger, and cold, to the envoys of Phraates, who approached them with perfidious offers of peace. "No," answered these loyal soldiers, turning their backs to the tempters, "we would rather eat bark and shells with Antony than abandon his cause."

The lieutenants were of the same mind. They sympathized with the splendid ambitions of their chief. Many of his officers had been taken into his confidence during the long night-watches in his tent, and these young men were imbued with the spirit of warfare and hoped to achieve brilliant records. The greater part of them had been impoverished by civil wars and revolutions, and they were counting on the fortunes of war to retrieve their losses, so they fought with the eager expectation of gamblers.

This was the material that Antony had collected for his first campaign into Persia; an invasion which in spite of wonderful deeds had brought him but scant success. At the outset, he had been compelled to tread cautiously in a country where the enemy had a powerful army already installed, whereas he had to bring his forces with him. Deceived alike by his naturally hopeful nature and by the reports which his couriers had brought after a superficial survey of conditions, he had imagined that the mere entrance of the Roman army into this ancient empire of Darius would make its worn-out granite walls crumble into dust.

When the real battles began he saw very clearly that the Medes, Parthians, and Armenians had lost none of their valour. He realized this cruelly at Phaaspa, where, by a totally unlooked-for turn of tactics, the enemy compelled him to alter his lines and raise the siege. More cruelly still was their prowess brought home to him during the retreat that he was forced to make at the beginning of winter, through a devastated country and under a shower of murderous arrows.

These calamities could have been avoided if his eagerness to return to Cleopatra had not made him hasten operations which required the most careful preparation. He came back from his festival of love, however, provided with new troops, reënforced artillery, and fresh supplies. The campaign met with greater success this time. He vanquished the Armenians, forced King Phraates to surrender to him the standards formerly set up by the legions of Crassus, and thus was able to send the Senate a glowing account of his movements, which passed in Rome for the flaming breath of victory.

While Antony in the plains of Erzerum was giving these proofs of his genius and daring, Octavius, no less determined to gain the supremacy, was seeking the means to place it within his grasp. War was not his strong point. At heart a coward, he preferred intrigue to action. He knew, however, that in Rome arms represented the standard of all grandeur, and he forced himself to consider them. Besides, circumstances left him no choice. His colleagues were at war; the one in Asia, the other in the African provinces. It rested with him to repulse the invasions of Sextus Pompey. By good luck, in spite of numerous defeats, his victory in Sicilian waters, whereby he won one hundred and sixty vessels from the pirate fleet, enabled him to announce before the Senate his delivery of the Republic from a formidable enemy, almost at the same hour that Antony sent word of his triumph in Persia.

However, neither of these victories was sufficiently important to give either Triumvir definite ascendancy over the other. But, preceded by the eagles of Crassus, whose downfall had been such a bitter blow to Roman pride, with the spoils that he had captured from the enemy, and leading among his captives the King Artabazes, together with his Queen and her children, Antony arrived at Rome. Crowned with golden laurels, driving along the Via Sacra in his chariot drawn by the four white horses that had borne Cæsar, Sulla, Marius, and the Scipios, he had addressed the crowd, saying: "I am master now, who knows who will come after me?"

It was not only in the army that Antony was popular. His good nature, his frankness, his consideration, and the scrupulous care that he gave to rewarding any service rendered him, had made friends for him everywhere, particularly among the townspeople. His absence, so far from destroying his prestige, had increased it, for in periods of unrest the people are apt to lay the blame of all mishaps on the Government in power, while they exaggerate the greatness of these who are gaining victories at a distance. If Antony had taken advantage of his opportunity and brought his trophies to Rome the day after his conquest of Media, and, like a good Roman citizen, prostrated himself before the statue of Jupiter, there is no doubt whatever that the imperial crown, refused to Cæsar, would have eventually been placed on his head. But, as wise old Homer has said, "What can be expected of a man who lets himself be the slave of a woman?"

To prevent his eluding her, Cleopatra had gone to meet her lover on the coast of Asia. She profited by the occasion to investigate her various interests there. Judea had a special fascination for her. That Judea of which she had not been able to obtain possession, but whose king paid her millions in tribute. Perhaps, too, she had a curiosity to meet the beautiful Mariamne, who was reputed to have such an irresistible fascination for Herod.

It was not without dire misgivings that these sovereigns learned of the forthcoming visit to their household of the bold and dangerous mistress of Antony. To be sure, it was protected by their faithful devotion, as well as by the holy memory of the Queen of Sheba's visit to Solomon, but Cleopatra's reputation was widespread. She, however, was too well aware of the relations between Herod and Antony to run any risk of offending the former. It was even whispered that she had a natural feminine desire to try her witcheries on the reputedly invulnerable heart of Judea's King, and that these coquetries came very near ending her life.

Like all women in love, Mariamne was morbidly jealous. She was furious at the intrusion of a woman, less beautiful perhaps than herself, but whose rich bronze hair, milk-white skin, and shining dark eyes had led astray the hearts of so many men. One evening when they had retired to their own apartments, after having been entertained by a series of songs and dances from Cleopatra, in which she had displayed all her marvellous power to charm, Mariamne observed that her husband was absent-minded. Promptly her thoughts flew to the sorceress of Egypt, and her smouldering suspicion kindled into flame: "You are thinking of her!" roared the enraged lioness, and heedless of Herod's sincere denial she demanded that Cleopatra be put to death on the instant.

To kill the Queen of Egypt! The ally of Rome! Such an act would entail fatal consequences. If Herod demurred it was not because his bloodthirsty soul baulked at either poison or poignard. It was not because the siren songs had touched his senses. No, he too hated her, for her yoke weighed heavily on his avaricious soul. He desired to get rid of her, but he scarcely dared run so tremendous a risk.

Mariamne used all the wiles of the serpent of Eden; she coaxed, she cajoled: "Do you not see that this woman is a menace to the whole world? Antony himself would be safer if he were free!" But the King was difficult to move. He argued, he resisted, and finally chose the part of prudence. In place of the amorous homage that she had been hoping to call forth, he loaded her with valuable gifts, and, without letting her suspect how near she had come to losing her life, he escorted her to the frontier, like a respectful vassal.

During those days that Cleopatra had spent near the Temple of Temples had this learned pupil of Apollodorus any desire to read the sacred books? Did she understand that the time for the birth of the Messiah was drawing near? Had she any intuition that out of this land of Judea, which she was oppressing like a despot, would rise the new sovereignty of Christianity from the ruins of the world of her day? Did she see the end of that civilization of which she was the fairest representative? Probably not, for, like all those who are devoured by ambition, Cleopatra thought only of her own aggrandizement, of the fulfilment of her glorious dreams. It would have been inconceivable to her mind, reared in the traditions of Egypt and of Greece, that what had taken centuries to build up would vanish like a bit of straw.

Besides, this was the time for hopeful visions rather than for misgivings. Antony was returning as victor. It was the moment to announce their marriage, to prove her sole dominion over the mighty conqueror. She awaited him eagerly, trembling with joyful anticipation.

When Antony caught sight of her on the Libyan slopes, a flower amongst flowers, her arms outspread to welcome him, her luscious mouth ready for his kisses, all thought of his duty to Rome was effaced in a moment. He saw her alone; his idol, his beloved, and his only wish was to follow where she led, to share his triumphs with her, and to add to her kingdoms the new kingdoms that he had just conquered. A squadron awaited them at the mouth of the Orontes and they set sail for Alexandria.

It was beyond belief that a Roman general should fail to bring the spoils of war to Rome. It was for Rome alone that he had fought and conquered. To Rome only belonged the privilege of conferring the triumph. But Antony had a reckless disregard for all these traditions. He was drunk with the homage of the Orient; her prostrate kings, her incense, the statues that she had erected in his honour. He felt a veritable giant and he meant to show his pride of achievement by an act of outrageous audacity. He planned to duplicate, on the banks of the Nile, the magnificent ceremonies with which Rome welcomed her returning conquerors on the banks of the Tiber.

Egyptian splendour equalled, if it did not exceed, that of Rome. On this occasion everyone was anxious to contribute his share to the gorgeous spectacle, for the insult to the Italian capital aroused keen delight in the heart of the Alexandrians. Every house was decorated; every citizen brought offerings; every woman wore her finest apparel and all her available jewels. It was a variegated crowd that assembled on the parade grounds to greet the Victor.

Suddenly there was a deep roar, as though the sea were pouring in. A thousand trumpets rang out and the victorious army marched into sight. The cavalry, in sparkling armour, led the way. Then the chariots shook the ground as they rolled by in martial splendour, laden with gold, silver, statues, all the spoils taken from the violated temples. Thousands of captives, with arms bound and heads bent, followed. Then King Artabazes, his wife and their two sons, appeared, their arms fastened with silver chains in token of their former grandeur. At last, standing in his chariot drawn by four foaming chargers, his brow crowned with golden laurel, superb in his robes of royal purple, came the Imperator.

On a platform draped with sumptuous silk, Cleopatra awaited him, her children by her side. On the first step stood Cæsarion, his face, even more than his name, recalling the divine Cæsar. No ceremony in Cleopatra's day had even approached this in royal grandeur, and surely no other one had ever held such a triumph for her. What it meant for this proud woman, who had borne the scoffs and jeers of Rome, to see its highest dignitaries prostrate at her feet! What a revenge to count by hundreds their golden eagles! In order to leave no doubt as to her intention of putting herself in the place of their god, Jupiter, she was wearing the silver tiara, surmounted by the sacred asp, which was the head-dress of her own goddess, Isis.

As the Imperator appeared she rose, advanced to the edge of the platform, and handed him the lotus sceptre, the replica of her own, in token that he was to share with her the throne of Egypt.

Antony's face was radiant. From his exalted stand he proclaimed her Queen of Kings, Empress, Goddess, and announced once more her sovereignty over the kingdoms which he had recently presented to her. Turning to the children, whose young heads were weighed down by their diadems, he explained the order of their inheritance. The eldest was to have Media, Armenia, and the land of the Parthians. Helios would inherit the Libyan provinces; and his twin sister, Selene, Phœnicia and the island of Cyprus. Cæsarion, who had just reached his fourteenth year and laid aside the white and purple robe of the Roman youth for the toga of manhood, he declared to be the sole heir of his father, Julius Cæsar.

There was deafening applause, as though Alexandria with her group of prospective kings was indeed the capital of all the world.

The sun dropped into the sea. From the gates of Canopus to the Necropolis, the line of houses began to show lights, one by one, in the gathering darkness, their roofs glowing red from the glare of the torches. All sorts of festivities began. Oil, wine, and wheat were distributed to the eager crowds; handfuls of money were thrown to the populace and gathered up as quickly as it fell. The huge tables in the palace gardens were loaded with refreshments. There were spectacles of every variety, noble and obscene, artistic and bloody, to suit all manner of tastes. The arena, as always, attracted the larger number of people. The animals had been let loose, and, with a license never permitted in Rome, young aristocrats took the part of the gladiators. When these contestants whetted the appetite of the wild beasts by offering their bare arms the whole audience stood up and watched, breathless, to see the blood gush out.

Following the Roman custom, these fêtes went on for forty days. On the opening evening Cleopatra and Antony appeared in their royal robes, apart—as befitted their position as sovereigns. Mounted on elephants, gleaming with jewels, they went through the different quarters of the city. But they soon wearied of this imposing regalia; it isolated them, kept them at a distance from the various amusements whose echoes appealed to their desire for entertainment. They dismissed the elephants and attendants and went about on foot through the paved streets. Once there, the feverish need for further excitement that stirs all merry-makers in Saturnalia took possession of them. They mixed with the rioters, enjoying their ribald jests and gross pleasures, and heedless of all sense of dignity, they wandered about as in the old days when they frequented the disreputable resorts of the Rhakotis.

Drink and excitement had stolen Antony's senses, and he conceived the grotesque notion of ending the festival with a gigantic orgy and masquerade, where, disguised as Silenus, surrounded by a crowd of bacchanals, he would wander through the streets all night long. There is a legend that owing to an amethyst ring, given to her by one of her necromancers, Cleopatra never lost her presence of mind. She chose the moment when Antony was utterly intoxicated to add a final insult to those that had been heaped upon Rome during this festival of folly. Mimics, eunuchs, the lowest kind of actors, were mounted on curules, the ivory chairs of state reserved for the highest dignitaries, and, in ridicule of a revered Roman custom, the Queen ordered all the Romans then in Alexandria to file past this rabble.

This scandal crowned the succession of orgies. When the news of it reached Octavius his heart quivered with delight! It supplied the means, which he had lacked the wit to devise, to undermine Antony's prestige. Careful and cunning, he suppressed his first instinct to make use of these outrages at once for his own advantage. It was not the right moment to attack an adversary who, in spite of blatant faults, had many warm partisans. Before beginning this assault he must win favour for himself and dispel the unflattering impressions that he had made in his youth. Versed in the trick of changing his policy, he effected such a complete alteration of standards that to this day it is uncertain which represented his real self: the cruel, suspicious, perfidious tyrant that he had seemed up to that time, or the gracious prince, the patron of art and letters, who has been known for so many centuries as Augustus Cæsar!

Cheating and trickery unquestionably played a part in this sudden metamorphosis, but it is possible that, seeing the wisdom of honesty, he used it as an instrument for promoting his own interests. At all events, if he were not a better man, his conduct from that time gave every evidence of it.

There was general astonishment on his return from Sicily. In place of the atrocious bloody reprisals which had stained Rome after the victory of Philippi, an amnesty was declared, with proposals of peace, a reduction of taxes, and various changes for the benefit of all classes of the people. Was not this the surest way to win favour? Instead of setting himself up in opposition to his rival, to give the people a season of wise moderation, as a contrast to the mad debauchery of Antony?

He carried out this idea by proclaiming his wish to reëstablish the simple manners and customs of former times. Recalling the austere principles of Cato, he forbade the wearing of the imperial purple by the people, restricting its use to the Senators. He suppressed money-changing and encouraged agricultural pursuits. He laid the foundation of the temple of Apollo on the Palatine hill, in order to furnish employment for the masons. Though not completed until many years later, this great religious work has always been associated with his name. And, most important of all, he decided to destroy Lepidus, because of the general contempt he had incurred on account of his merciless raids to accumulate wealth for his own use. This limiting of the Government to two rulers was universally welcomed. It was a sign of ultimate republican unity, the first blow at the accursed Triumvirate.

In all these movements Octavius had been aided by his friends' counsel. He had many warm friends, for the gods are generous in according this blessing to men not otherwise specially gifted, who are thereby able to accomplish great things. Three of these friends assumed all responsibility and bore him, on the wings of their devotion, to heights which otherwise he could never have reached. These were Theodorus, the learned teacher, on whose keen judgment he could always rely in difficult undertakings; Agrippa, that incomparable warrior, a veritable Neptune, who had complete command of the seas; and Mæcenas, above all, the wise, the charming Mæcenas, whose tactful, subtle intelligence was such that in giving counsel or advice he always made his opponents believe that they themselves had originated the idea.

Octavius fully understood the value of their support and undertook nothing without consulting them. When he heard of what was going on at Alexandria he summoned them at once. Each one, though consulted privately as to what should be done in reply to Antony's insulting actions, had the same view. They were of one mind. Assuredly Antony had brought only anathemas upon his head, but his name, a synonym for glory, generosity, courage, was greatly beloved; to make a direct attack upon this popular hero would be unwise. She who had shared in his evil deeds, however, they could safely condemn, being sure of the commendation of the people; feared, as well as scorned, Cleopatra, in the eyes of the Romans, was responsible for all these outrages. It was rumoured that she had put secret potions in the wine which had robbed Antony of his reason. It was finally decided to ignore for the moment any part that the Imperator had taken in these scandalous proceedings and to rouse the people against her, whom they venomously termed "the Sorceress of the Nile!"

The method of temporizing which Octavius embodied in his motto: *"Sat celeriter quidquid fiat satis bene,"* had up to that time been highly successful. Accordingly he proceeded slowly and, while waiting to attack his actual adversary, he commanded Theodorus to open a campaign of accusations against the Egyptian Queen.

The Romans were always easily roused. Devoted to their capital city, it was enough for them to hear that it was in any way criticized: a suspicion, a suggestion, that it was in peril was sufficient to stir them profoundly. These proud citizens of Rome had the idea that all other great cities envied her and were anxious to overthrow her power. Carthage, Corinth, Athens, all in important positions, had in their turn fallen under suspicion. To-day all their instincts of defence were united against superb, preëminent Alexandria. There was a persistent rumour that Cleopatra was planning to transfer the world-capital from Rome to that city. This danger in itself would have bred hatred of her, but, in addition, there were the recent vile tales. Her extravagant luxury was especially distasteful to a people who made poverty almost a crime. In passing from mouth to mouth the incident of the pearls was naturally exaggerated. There was now an account of a bath, enriched each day by a mixture of gold and amber, to which the body of this courtesan owed the glowing warmth of colour which so enticed men's gaze.

While this gossip was spreading among the Plebeians, Mæcenas was busy agitating the Intellectuals. He got together a group of literary men, and, with that ease of language and charm of persuasion that always carried conviction, he described Octavius as the coming master of the world. These men were quickly persuaded to use their pens to advance his cause. It was arranged to make conservatism, religion, devotion, social reform the fashion—all the ideals of which Cæsar's nephew was patron, as opposed to the Oriental usages to which Antony had become a convert. Virgil, in his delightful pastoral, was the first to carry out this project of Mæcenas's. His poems were of wide influence in reviving that taste for country life and love of the earth which the long wars had rudely interrupted. At the same time Horace put aside his Epodes on wine and women for the more serious Odes. Deploring the fatal power of women when in control of the Government by actual right or by their domination over the men who represented it, he gave an outline of the lives of women famous in history and legend, and set forth the inevitable misfortune that they had brought upon their countries. He adjured the people, in the name of their imperilled nation, to unite against the fatal Egyptian woman, the evil demon of the day.

The situation was growing less difficult for Octavius. He could now venture to lay before the Senate certain accusations that until that moment he had not dared to make public. The Senate was the supreme arbiter, the tribunal before which all discussions relating to the Government were laid. To denounce his colleague there was dangerous, for not only had Antony many partisans in the Senate, but this year the two Consuls, Caius Sossius and Ahenobarbus, were his sworn friends. The advisers of Octavius were well aware of the risks incurred, but, under the existing conditions, immediate action was imperative. A duel to the death must be fought between the two rivals.

It was one of the last days of the year 33 B. C. The sun went in and out amongst the flake-like clouds, making it impossible to know whether sunshine or cloud-drifts would prevail. Octavius studied the sky long and earnestly and finally decided that the way the birds were flying meant weather favourable for his undertaking. He started toward the Senate.

The crowd had begun to gather. There were beggars asking alms and slaves carrying provisions. Women were collected about the public marketplaces where beans, fish, and sausages were displayed. Half-naked children, brown as crickets, paddled in the gutters. Troops of donkeys, bearing wicker baskets, chariots, litters, blocked the streets. Twelve lictors ran before the Imperator to clear the way, but in spite of that his pallor and nervousness were noticed by the people in the street. He was under a strain, and as he took his seat in the chair of honour he felt beneath his toga for the poignard which he always carried there. Since the assassination of Cæsar a *senatus consulte* had forbidden the wearing of arms in the Senate chamber. But to-day, on the eve of a debate, the consequences of which no one could divine, all precautions were legal. At least so Octavius thought!

At the first instant the opposing parties gauged each other at a glance. Placing a heavy portfolio before him, filled with his various accusations against Antony, Octavius opened the discussion. Faithful to his former tactics, which had been so successful with the people, he launched his opening diatribes against Cleopatra:

"This incestuous daughter of Ptolemy the Piper, descendant of the Lagidæ, is our worst enemy. Threatened in her own country by those who abhor her loose ways and the dangers of her insecure government, she has made use of the power of Rome for her own protection. Intoxicated with her success, this mad woman has even dreamed of destroying our capital. She is preparing to attack us, I tell you, and with a shameful army of slaves and eunuchs is planning an invasion of Italy!"

The effect of this speech was instantaneous. The uproar that greeted it was deafening. Furious with rage, the Senators rose in a body, and with angry gestures raised their togas like the wings of gigantic, ferocious birds.

A direct attack on Antony required greater courage. Octavius felt that the least false step might result in an irreparable downfall. Confident, however, of the convincing force of his arguments, he commenced his address. He denounced Antony, not only for having taken for his own use the newly acquired provinces, but for having deliberately made over the greater part of them to the Queen of Egypt.

"Yes, not content with robbing and despoiling his own country, this infatuated lover of Cleopatra has offered to this alien woman Armenia and Media, the territories of Calcida, as well as Phœnicia, with Tyre and Sidon, and the enormous revenues from Palestine." Octavius paused between the name of each country in order to let the wrath of the people have ample time to seek expression. The protestations came with precipitate and overwhelming violence.

"The scoundrel! The traitor! Our beautiful lands! Our richest provinces!" Shouts of indignation filled the hall.

Until that moment Antony's staunch supporters had thought it wise to keep silence. When the first roars began to subside Caius Sossius commanded silence. He announced an important proclamation. That very morning he had received a notice that would give the lie direct to these attacks, which the conqueror of the Parthians had fully expected. In eloquent terms, the Consul recalled the recent brilliant deeds of Mark Antony. "And," he thundered, "it is he, the valiant hero of all these victories, whose life has been risked again and again for the glory of his country, for the safety of Rome, who is now being villified because he is not here to defend himself!"

The tide changed on the instant. "It is cowardly! It is unworthy of us," cried a dozen voices. Encouraged by this evidence of sympathy, Sossius went on with greater emphasis. "These much decried donations to Alexandria, what are they but annexations of Rome? As Egypt is, or will be to-morrow, a Roman province, why is there any discontent? This wealth of the Orient, what is it used for? It is equipping the Roman army, feeding the soldiers of the Republic. It is building temples, it is erecting barracks, to make the name of our Capital revered throughout the world! Where is our loss?"

"Moreover," continued the friend of Antony, with a respectful inclination to the august assembly, "in regard to the rights of the Senate, the Imperator requests that you either ratify the measures that he has taken in the service of his country, or, if you disapprove of his action in the matter, to turn them down."

The tide had unmistakably turned in Antony's favour. Whatever errors he had committed in his infatuation for Cleopatra, he had been the dominant figure in Roman warfare during the past ten years; the only one who had accomplished great deeds and who had been, through all, a noble citizen of Rome.

Octavius felt the ground giving way beneath his feet. Pale as the statues around him, he felt as though after this first tilt he might probably end with his head in the dust. His swelling portfolio, however, was still full of accusations against Antony. His weapons were not yet exhausted. He took his courage in both hands and again began to speak. He went over the deeds of Antony and Cleopatra during the festivities at Alexandria, giving, in exaggerated and revolting detail, the experiences of those nights of debauchery in the streets of the great city. He dwelt on the investiture of Cleopatra's bastard children, especially the fact that Cæsarion was treated with the honour and ceremony belonging to a Roman prince in being presented to the Roman legions as the lawful heir of Cæsar.

Here there was an interruption. Why harp on an old grievance? The Republic was not a dynasty, there was no sense in taking umbrage at so-called heirs. All that was merely part of the masquerading. If Antony had joined in such frivolous amusements it was regrettable certainly, it showed a lack of dignity. But, on the other hand, the same thing had occurred at Rome, when he had had his chariot drawn by lions. Such puerile nonsense was ridiculous but scarcely deserving of severe reproof.

The current was propitious now and Sossius took advantage of it to remind the people that the policy of Octavius, at the time of Cæsar's death, had been reprehensible in the extreme. Here Tufius interposed with the comment that it was useless to recur to things so far in the past.

"I speak of the things of yesterday," retorted the Consul. He then explained briefly that in destroying the Triumvirate and altering it into a dictatorship for two, Octavius had appropriated for himself the share belonging to Lepidus. In seizing the African provinces, with their ships, cavalry, infantry, and all their accessories; in confiscating for his personal use the Sicilian land wrested from Sextus Pompey; in dividing the best parts of Italy among his own soldiers, leaving no portions for the veterans of the other armies, had not Octavius offended justice and exceeded the limits of his power far more than Antony had ever done?

Another outburst, equalling the one provoked by the opening speech of Octavius, began. The assembly was completely won over to Antony's cause. Sweat stood in great drops on the forehead of Octavius. He felt the sheath of his hidden poignard press against his left side. For the moment he had the sensation of being trapped, and with clenched teeth and flaming eyes he glared about him defiantly. He was accused of aspiring to the office of supreme magistrate! How could he give irrefutable proof of his disinterestedness?

"I will resign every office that I hold; I will give up all public duties and go back to private life as a plain Roman citizen, on the sole condition that my colleague, Antony, does the same!" he cried.

This struck the right note. Every one was weary of the dictatorship and wanted to return to a republican form of government. But the issues then at stake were too grave to permit a hasty decision. Besides, Octavius did not have the confidence of the people. His former attitude had given good ground for suspicion. The very moment when he was ostensibly giving up his power might be precisely the instant when he was exploiting his position in order to retain it.

Undecided as to what was to be the next step, the Consuls declared that in Antony's absence immediate action was impossible. A conference with him was essential. Ahenobarbus proposed going to Alexandria to obtain his resignation. The majority endorsed this course and the vote was held over for a later meeting.

The situation was perplexing for Octavius. Again he realized how deep a hold Antony had on the affections of the people. It was the same old story. How could he hope to defeat a rival who had not only a formidable army at his back, but wealth and popularity in addition? He went to consult his friends, as he always did when in a quandary.

Mæcenas lived in a villa on the Esquiline hill, commanding a magnificent view. Rome lay in majestic state on the banks of her river below, and the soft beauty of the Campagna stretched out to the Sabine Hills along the horizon. As Octavius drew near Mæcenas went out to meet him with outstretched hands. His affection for the Imperator was sincere and loyal, as is shown in various letters from him. "I love you better than myself. Where you lead, I will follow. Whatever comes to you I will share, for my life is inseparably bound up in yours."

The two friends sat down near the brazier, which filled the hall with warmth and the fragrance of incense. Octavius recounted what had just happened in the Senate. Mæcenas admitted that there were grave difficulties, but he contended that these were only temporary and that they could be adjusted. In Antony's present state of over-excitement he would undoubtedly do something to rouse keen disapproval, if not a serious disturbance. In the meantime Agrippa should make secret preparations for war, while Octavius devised some means of turning the tide of public opinion once more in his favour. A policy of strict conservatism, as opposed to the wild Egyptian schemes of Antony, seemed the wise move at the moment. The oldest temple in Rome, that built in the time of Romulus in honour of Jupiter Feretrius, was falling into ruins. Octavius must give orders for its reconstruction. He must also complete the building of the Pantheon, begun by Cæsar to the glory of Mars.

While the two friends were planning for the future, Athenodorus came in. His practical mind confirmed these suggestions. He proposed that they consider something to please the Plebeians, for their opinion carried great weight as to popularity. During the summer months the Roman populace suffered cruelly from scarcity of water. It would be an excellent device to repair the aqueduct of Marcia, and to open cheap baths, in order that the working classes might have the same comfort and refreshment that the Patricians enjoyed in their luxurious *sudatoria*.

These constructive works met Octavius's entire approval. In the near future they might prove to be his strongest support. But the moment was not propitious for the carrying out of the plans. He had barely had time to summon the architects and go over their drawings, when a thunderbolt fell!

Unknown to Cleopatra, Antony had always kept up friendly relations with Octavia. In the first place, he was really grateful for all the assistance that this noble woman had rendered him. In the second, he had the more powerful motive of expecting further services! They exchanged letters frequently, and, as the sister of Octavius, she could keep her husband fully informed of all that was going on in Rome. She was, in addition, the most desirable of mediators, for her delicate hands held the thread of communication between the brothers-in-law and she was careful not to break it off. She also constantly entertained a set of Antony's friends in her house on the Palatine hill, and these were always ready to discuss the virtues of their hero and do honour to him in his absence. With warm affection she had looked after the education not only of her own children, but of those that Fulvia had borne Antony as well.

Unlucky chance, or one of those acts of treachery that often occur in the nests of intrigue which form in kings' palaces, had thrown one of Antony's letters to his wife into the hands of Cleopatra. Its affectionate tone and the promise of a visit in the near future precipitated a crisis which was bound to come. In the Queen's heart, uneasy always with memories and fears, the arrow of jealousy struck deep. "After all he has promised me!" she cried bitterly. Then came the inevitable reaction, natural to a highly strung, nervous nature that could endure no grief, and again she cried: "I will have my revenge!"

Charmian, who never left her side, lived in a perpetual state of terror. She was divided between love for the Queen and dread of her passionate temperament that was always courting dramatic situations. Had not an augur predicted that the love affair of Antony and Cleopatra would end in blood? She longed to divert her beloved mistress from the passion that threatened to drive her mad. Kneeling before her, she laid her head on the Queen's trembling knees. "Why should you suffer thus?" she said. The girl felt her shoulder warm from the Queen's feverish touch. "If I could only hold that cursed woman here in my hands and by a thousand tortures make her expiate the sufferings she has brought me!" Cleopatra's voice shook with rage. Charmian tried to calm her, but the wound was already festering and the venom of hate was spreading through her veins. With a sudden frenzy she included the whole world in her vengeance as she swore: "I will go to Rome itself. I will compel Octavius and his sister to go to war, and with bound hands she shall follow my chariot to the Capitol!"

This extravagant fancy was distressing to Charmian. As in a mist she saw the deadly whirlpool sucking them all down in its depths. But wise counsel is impotent in dealing with a mind wild with jealous desire to seize and rend its prey. Charmian's gentle words were not regarded.

The afternoon was nearly over. The air grew less stifling and fresh puffs of fragrance were wafted in from the magnolia trees. All the shades of the rainbow shone in the sunset light. It was the hour when Antony, refreshed and perfumed, after his daily siesta, came to seek Cleopatra. She was lying on her couch and, annoyed at his being a little late for their rendezvous, she put her elbow on the sumptuous cushions and held her head as though it were heavy with aching. His step made her tremble, and she had a sullen, troubled expression that indicated a coming storm.

Antony had no chance to escape. The fatal letter, unrolled from its mother-of-pearl rod, lay on the table. For this letter, for his crime of being friendly with his faithful wife, he would have to pay dearly. As he drew near she overwhelmed him with a flood of violent reproaches. He was a man who could not keep his word. While she, happy in their being together, and awaiting impatiently the coming announcement of their marriage, was full of trust in him, he was playing her false, planning to leave her. He listened silently, and when her first outburst had subsided he tried to plead with her. The political situation compelled him to maintain cordial relations with the sister of Octavius, as she was the most valuable and dependable intermediary in his connections with the Government at Rome. Her help was necessary for the protection of his interests there. If he severed this alliance it would entail a war for which he was not prepared. But Cleopatra paid no heed. She was burning with jealousy and a desire for vengeance. She would put an end, once and for all, to this rival who had alienated Antony's affections. She would require that Antony, by an official repudiation of Octavia, should break the last bond that held him to the Occident, and thenceforth he should belong to her alone.

Antony was fresh from an interview with Ahenobarbus, who had arrived at Alexandria the day before, bringing news of the active campaign against him that was going on in Italy and warning him of the consequence of his continued stay in Egypt. If the thunderbolts that had been let loose in the Senate had been turned aside it was solely due to the loyalty of his friends there, but they had defended him because they were counting on his speedy return to Rome, on his skill in handling the situation when he came. They would brook no insult to his noble wife. She had the entire sympathy of the State and he would offend public opinion if he dared to put the Egyptian woman in her place. No one would come to his defence a second time. Patricians and Plebeians alike would be on the side of Octavius and his sister, and their warm sentiments would be roused in behalf of the abandoned wife and her children.

In a gleam of reason, the last perhaps that this warrior-statesman ever knew, Antony saw clearly the dire results of his carrying out the demand of his fierce mistress. Quivering with excitement he tried to ward off the coming tragedy.

"We must be cautious. What demon of jealousy possesses you? The astounding rupture that you are asking me to make will in no way affect our mutual relations. All my life is yours, and only yours. I have no thought but to serve you!"

But Cleopatra was too enraged to listen to reason. With her long, snake-like eyes, her luscious scarlet mouth, her body curled in a corner of her divan, she seemed like an impregnable fortress.

"I will not yield. I have had enough of hearing

the Romans call Octavia your wife and me your concubine. I desire that by a solemn, official deed you proclaim me, Cleopatra, as your only lawful wife."

The struggle this time was neither so long nor so violent as the one of three years before when Antony, moved by the tender devotion of Octavia, had defended her against his mistress. To-day, far away, given over to a life of uninteresting virtue, she had less power to hold his affection. Cleopatra's insatiable passion won the victory and led to that entire subjugation of will in which a man is no longer a man. His spirit as well as his flesh was conquered. He was as wax in her hands, and when she asserted that Octavia had always been the secret ally of her brother, and that both at Tarentum and at Rome Antony had been their plaything, he made no protest and his silence was like acquiescence. But that was not enough. To gain all she wanted it was necessary to rouse in Antony a passionate hatred, and as this would not have been possible against the tender, loving wife who had been so faithful to him, she brought up the name of Octavius to awaken all the fierce animosity in his soul. To a man of his temperament, impressionable, weak, but devoured with ambition, she held up the poltroon Octavius as the man who was seizing the supreme power.

"So you will be content with our little eastern kingdom," she sneered, "while he holds dominion over all the countries from Illyria to the Pillars of Hercules!"

Antony's cheeks blanched. This vision of his colleague's outranking him, possessing greater power, master of vaster territories than his own, sent a shiver through his whole being. Such hatred must have an outlet. Twice already these rivals had been at the point of flying at each other's throats; of destroying each other; twice the tiny hand of a woman had intervened. To-day it was again a woman's hand that slipped in between them, but this time to stir up anger, to corrupt, to embitter, and this time war was inevitable.

IX

Actium

OCTAVIUS had just come, as he did every few days, to see his sister. Although there was always an affectionate intimacy between them, to-day their voices were raised in a manner that suggested a difference of opinion, if not a sharp disagreement. The subject under discussion was the usual one, and the more Octavius accused Antony the more Octavia defended him.

"Antony is not so much in the wrong as you say. I understand his motives. He writes often. I know how dear Rome is to him, that he adores his children. Besides, we shall soon see him here."

"How can you deceive yourself so? Are you blind, my sister, to the infamous way he has treated you? Have you forgotten that he sent you back from Athens like a servant, without honour, without escort, without even the thanks that your generosity toward him deserved?"

No, Octavia had forgotten nothing, but her loving heart was ready to excuse all rather than lose the one she loved.

But Octavius had come to-day to make clear to her a plan which, personally, was not agreeable to him. Before publicly denouncing Antony he believed that he should first separate his wife from him, and make her an ally against the rival whom he wished to annihilate. He recounted Antony's shameful submission to the Egyptian, and dwelt upon the scandalous records of his life in Alexandria. How could he be so brutal? Why did not Octavia's sensitive face, reddening at the vile details, turning away, tortured, disarm this executioner? Pitilessly he went on. He wanted to search the very depths of her heart to find its tenderest spot. "One day, on the parade grounds, with officers and soldiers bearing arms, the staff surmounted by the golden eagle in his hand, the Imperator was reviewing the troops. Suddenly a messenger approached and said a few words. Immediately, disregarding the military display arranged by his order, he left the grounds to rejoin Cleopatra, who had summoned him from no other motive than the caprice of being obeyed by one who was commanding so many men! Another time he was in the prætorium. The Tetrarch of Judea was bringing up some important questions in litigation. Antony alone was able to decide these, but he heard the royal litter coming and it acted like a wave of madness. Without listening to another word he fled from the assembled judges and was seen no more that day.

Octavius would have gone on indefinitely, for the list, more or less true, of Antony's misdeeds in Egypt was a long one, but his sister stopped him.

"It is enough; he has grave faults but he is my husband. He only has the right to break the tie that unites us. As long as he does not break it I will wait and hope." And though her voice trembled, her expression showed that her determination was not to be shaken.

A few days later this noble woman heard that Cleopatra's lover had repudiated his lawful wife! Nothing had availed; neither her generous goodness, her patience under indignities, nor that hope which is the heart's armour against the menace of destiny, nothing had prevented the fatal blow!

Poor Octavia! The home which her marriage had made her own, the room where in Antony's arms she had known happiness, the table where his deep laughter had made good cheer, the garden where they had breathed together the rich fragrance of summer evenings, she had to leave them all, to part with them for ever. The overwhelming sorrow left her listless, inert, like an instrument whose string is broken.

Octavius, who lost no chance to forward his own interest, and for whose personal advantage each insult inflicted on his sister made capital, had summoned the crowd. Notified as to the day and hour that Octavia was to leave the palace, the throngs filled the entrances. When they saw her, surrounded by her children, her own as well as the son and daughter of Fulvia who had been left in her care, there was a great clamour. Her wrongs stirred their indignation, and scornful epithets were heard concerning the libertine who, for the sake of the Egyptian sorceress, had abandoned a wife of illustrious blood and noble character.

Octavia kept silence. She did not want Antony's name to be cursed on her account. With the idea of appeasing the crowd she held up her youngest son, who was the living image of his father. The unhappy woman hoped that the sight of this beautiful, innocent child might arouse some affection for the father.

Antony's divorcing the sister of Octavius was equivalent to a declaration of war. In spite of the totally different natures of the two Triumvirs, their rivalries, deceptions, the tricks they had played on each other, this gentle woman had been a powerful bond between them. With her and through her there had always been the hope of maintaining a balance. Now everything was upset. The violent shock had dislodged the masks and the bare faces showed fear.

Which would be master? Although the real cause of the quarrel was the desire for supremacy, there was now great pretence of its being a struggle for ideals. The words "honour," "patriotism," a "return to republican institutions," were in the mouths of the people. It was difficult to choose between two competitors when each claimed to be fighting to save the honour of the country. Octavius lied when he declared that he was ready to lay aside his power; and Antony was not honest when he stood forth as the champion of liberty. As in the great contentions between Cæsar and Pompey, the public was divided, each voter selecting the chief who seemed most likely to advance his interests. The feeling was such that even the children had their share in it. Athenodorus tells of seeing two little street urchins in a vigorous fisticuff. "Why are you beating each other like that?" he asked. "We are playing; I am

Octavius," replied one, who had just been chased to the edge of a ditch. "And I am Antony," joined in the other, tilting his little chin proudly.

Although the divorce had produced a most unfavourable impression and had lessened the number of Antony's partisans, yet public opinion was not altogether against him. His glorious past, his strength, his riches, made him an adversary to be feared, and one to be attacked only on ground that was wholly unprepared. To destroy his good name and to vilify him as the slave of Egypt's Queen was Octavius's policy.

However patient he had sworn to be, Octavius was growing tired of working underground like a mole, when suddenly the gods, who seemed on his side, sent him an unexpected assistant. Munatius Plancus, who in the Egyptian celebrations, clad in green silk and crowned with reeds, had played the rôle of Glaucus, "the handy man" as Cleopatra had scornfully called him, had just arrived in Rome. Whether from a desire to avenge his wounded vanity, or a capacity for seeing which way the wind was turning, this contemptible creature, suddenly separated from his former companions, told vile tales about them which made him a welcome guest in the halls of Rome. But this social success was not sufficient for a man as poverty-stricken as he was vulgar. He knew that a discovered treason would mean money to him, so he gained the ear of Octavius and told him about a document of great importance. It was the will which Antony had revised on the eve of his departure for Persia, a will making Cleopatra his sole heir, dividing the Oriental empire between her and her children, and, infatuated even in death, commanding that in whatever land he should die his body be transported to rest near his beloved mistress. Plancus did not have the actual document in his possession, for, faithful to his mission three years before, he had deposited it safely in the hands of the Vestal Virgins; but he knew every word of it and could reproduce it to the letter.

The Romans attached great importance to the ceremony of burial. It was their universal desire to rest near their own people, in the sacred ground of their ancestors, and where their children would lie in their turn. The thought of dying and of having their graves in foreign lands was horrible to all soldiers, and every one who could afford it left directions for his body to be brought back to Italy.

Of all Antony's follies through his mad love for Cleopatra, this desire to be buried in Egypt was the most detestable, and the one that influenced public opinion most bitterly. Octavius felt that if it were moved by this sacrilege he could count on rousing the wrath of the Senate and turning the vote against the author of such a crime. The difficulty was to procure the proof.

The Temple of Vesta, modelled after the one at Delphi, stood near the Forum, at the foot of the Palatine hill. Octavius had only to cross the Via Sacra to be at its doors. He set forth with an escort and preceded by twelve lictors, resplendent with the insignia of the Government. On reaching the entrance he signalled for them to remain without, and wrapped in his purple toga he mounted the sacred steps unattended.

The priestesses of Vesta lived in the shadow of the altars. They were young girls of noble birth, clad in snow-white robes with veils over their heads. They had profound reverence for their different duties. These consisted in keeping a perpetual flame burning before the altar, and guarding the Palladium, that sacred statue of Pallas Athene saved from burning Troy. They were held in such high esteem that whenever any of the Roman Pontiffs, Proconsuls, or Generals were called away from Rome, they confided their most precious treasures and priceless papers to their care, rather than risk the chances of travelling with them. For what safer place could be found than this temple whose guardians had for their motto the words: *"Die rather than break your oath."*

When Octavius made known the object of his visit these noble women were filled with righteous indignation. What! Give up anything left in their care! Be false to their faith! Betray the confidence which had relied on their word!

The wily visitor pleaded that in a case of service to one's country such scruples were absurd; but the Vestal Virgins were not to be persuaded. Force alone could drag from them what they had sworn to guard.

Octavius was cautious. His instincts were against using force, and besides, he feared the criticism which any abuse of his power might bring down on his head. Sometimes, however, necessity compels. The lictors outside the temple were called in; a few blows of a mallet, and the coffer that a warrior had trusted to guard his treasure gave up its secret.

In the Senate the reading of Antony's will produced the effect that Octavius had counted on. For his side it was a triumph. But Antony's friends were speechless with consternation. Was he so faithless to his country that he did not even wish to be buried there? Had he, in truth, ceased to be a Roman? Octavius, however, was severely criticized for his conduct. Caius Sossius laid stress on the shameful act. A will was sacred. No one had the right to question what a man ordered done after his death. Such interference was illegal; besides, a will could be changed at any time! Some Senators, faithful to the old traditions, held this view and were incensed at the outrage offered to the Vestal Virgins. The thing had been done, however, and its consequences were serious.

It was the moment to drive the dagger to the hilt. Octavius brought up all the old grievances. He emphasized the proof of Antony's disloyalty. There were additional charges. One of the surest means of transforming the rich Patricians who sat in the Senate into pitiless judges was to bring up any injustice done to Rome in regard to art. He held up Antony as a collector for the Queen of Egypt, who had robbed Greece and Asia of their rarest treasures in order to offer them to his mistress. The famous statue of Diana, once the glory of Ephesus, now adorned the portico of the Bruchium. The two hundred thousand volumes from the library of Pergamus, intended to enrich the Roman collection, had they not been shipped to Alexandria? A murmur ran around the Senate chamber. Ominous frowns were visible. All these men whose dwellings were enriched with books, rare furniture, beautiful marbles, collected in their travels or during their rule over various countries, were as indignant as though Antony's offence were without precedent. In hypocritical anger they demanded that a vote on his actions be taken without delay. The urns were passed, and flouted, scorned, pronounced unworthy of office, Antony was deprived of all the functions that the Republic had given into his keeping.

Complete as was the victory, it did not satisfy Octavius. These assemblies, as he well knew, were subject to quick and complete changes of attitude. What this wily tactician wanted was to give his adversary a killing blow from which he would never recover. A military victory was the only certain means of putting this conqueror of the Parthians definitely out of the running. But how could his compatriots be induced to take arms against him? They were tired of civil wars and nothing would be more distasteful than to rise against Mark Antony, the only great citizen who, since Cæsar, had made the Roman flag fly over new territories.

The same old subterfuge which had succeeded before was once more adroitly employed by Octavius. A few days later, leaving out any allusion to Antony in his address, not even mentioning that name which was always likely to create enthusiasm, he spoke of the indisputable enemy, the one that was certain to rouse public sentiment. The tiresome repetition of Cleopatra's ambition, her persistent intention of attacking Rome, these weapons had lost none of their power. The mere mention of her name created almost ferocious excitement. In a second the whole Senate was standing up, hurling curses on the hated Egyptian.

At last war was declared. Faithful to the custom consecrated by his ancestors, Octavius repaired to the square just beyond the Pomœrium, where the temple of Bellona, majestic and radiant, stood out against the clear blue of the sky. Amidst the acclamations of the wrought-up crowd the Dictator threw a gold javelin whose point sunk in the pedestal at the feet of the goddess. This ceremony was to place the army under her divine protection while declaring at the same time the righteousness of the campaign that had just begun.

Nominally the war was directed against foreign forces, but who could mistake its import? Antony was the protector of Cleopatra, and on both sides Roman blood would stain the battlefield.

Antony, however, had not awaited the challenge from Rome. Like the good captain that he was he had planned to forestall the enemy and take the offensive. Sixteen legions commanded by Canidius were ordered to the coast of Asia Minor, and he was on his way to join them. A sure means of refuting the libellous statements of Octavius occurred to him. He would put aside his mistress and appear alone at the head of his troops. That would show whom they had to fight.

But Cleopatra objected to this device. She had never forgotten what had happened when Antony left her once before. She would take no chance of having her lover caught a second time in a Roman trap. With his impressionable character it was necessary literally to keep him in full view, to perform continual incantations over him. So she refused to be separated from him. Where he went she went. He should plan no undertaking, no negotiation, without her knowledge and supervision. In vain the Imperator dwelt on the inconvenience of having a woman present in the camps. In vain Ahenobarbus, with characteristic rudeness, declared that if they were to be encumbered with a court he would retire. Through everything Cleopatra held to her resolution. "Whatever happens," she replied to the malcontents, "nothing shall separate me from Antony!"

A secret understanding between them doubtless enabled her to take this stand. In any case she acted with the unquestionable authority of one who supplied the ways and means. It was her unlimited wealth that paid the expenses of the campaign. It was her fleet of two hundred brave ships, well-armed and equipped, that prevented the enemy's attack in the Mediterranean. Whatever was behind it, her decision prevailed, and in the first days of spring, on board the galley *Antoniad*, which was decorated as for a fête, the enamoured pair embarked for the final stage of their destiny.

Never had the treacherous Mediterranean been clearer or more tranquil. The blue of sea and sky were blended in soft tones of azure. At sunset amber-coloured ripples passed over its surface, mingled with waves of rose. The sound of the wind in the sails toned in with the music from lyres and flutes. Nights of love followed the joyous days, and there was no hint of the fierce storm that was advancing toward the frail vessel.

This was only a prelude. At Samos, where they landed, at Ephesus, where they remained for some time, the lovers took up again the pomp and festivals of Alexandria. The old Asiatic town, accustomed though it was to luxury, had never seen such displays as these. Cortèges of kings, crowned with tiaras and clad in embroidered robes, came every day to Antony, bringing soldiers, horses, provisions, everything that could contribute to the success of his campaign. Desirous that they should carry back to their own countries an exalted impression of their sovereign, Cleopatra made every effort to outshine them. Each new arrival served as a pretext for a sumptuous display. Spectacle followed spectacle, and princes coming from distant lands to do battle were astonished to find, side by side with the iron-covered chests, brass chariots, and death-dealing engines, troops of acrobats, mountebanks, and their paraphernalia, totally out of place in camp life.

At the hour when the whole world was straining under the weight of armaments, when masses of people were on the point of collapse, when the fate of empires was in the balance, this was the way that the mistress of Mark Antony chose to flaunt her overweening faith that the victory would be hers.

Antony was far from sharing her confidence. The time for frivolity was over. He recognized the perils of his position. Divided between the urgent pleas of his comrades-in-arms, urging him to carry the war at once into Italy and give battle there before Octavius had time to concentrate his forces, and the fair sorceress who was coaxing him to dally, he was pulled both ways. It was a tremendous game and the chances were not in his favour. To play it successfully cool judgment was essential; and that had never been his strong point. The nervous excitement of his life with Cleopatra and the amorous demands of her jealous despotism had robbed him of what little he possessed. His generals added to his perplexities. They were convinced that their Imperator would never lead them to victory as long as he was under the malign influence of this woman, and they determined to compel her to leave the camp.

Ahenobarbus, as always, had the most courage and he took the initiative. He had an interview with the Queen, and, knowing the value of his disinterested services, he made no pretence of flattery, but declared brusquely that the confusion which her presence and that of the court was creating exceeded even his worst fears, and that her proper place was at Alexandria, where her ministers were calling for her. Although Antony was of the same mind, he was powerless against the beguilements of a mistress who responded to his most earnest arguments by embraces, kisses, and tears.

Cleopatra was more unwilling than ever to leave Antony exposed to the reproaches of those austere Romans who surrounded him. Harrowed by their insistence, would he be able to resist that reconciliation with Octavius which she knew many of them desired to bring about? In order to go on with her rôle of the warlike Egeria, some support was necessary. This she obtained, by promises and cajolings, from Canidius, the general who had most influence with Antony. He took the opposite side from that of Ahenobarbus, declaring that it was neither just nor wise to banish an ally whose gold, ships, and soldiers formed such an important part of their army; and, with the suavity of a courtier, added that he could not see how the counsels of a great Queen, who was as noble and brave as she was beautiful, could possibly harm an army whose courage she upheld by her own.

The opposing party was not beaten. The most ardent among them was Quintus Dellius, for he had all of Antony's interests at heart. This wise old juggler in politics had seen very quickly the schemes of the Egyptian and had realized that they were entirely contrary to his own advantage and that of his fellow Romans. He decided that at all hazards he would save his chief from his present peril, and without circumlocution he said:

"Cleopatra is leading us to ruin!"

Enraged at this accusation of the woman who held his heart as well as his reason in her hands, Antony cried:

"What are you saying? What right have you to make such an assertion?"

Dellius was ready with explanations which were summed up in his next speech:

"I tell you that this daughter of the Lagidæ does not bring, cannot bring the same soul to this war that we Romans have!"

"Cleopatra's interests and mine are one and the same," answered Antony, haughtily.

Dellius could not let that assertion pass.

"You are mistaken. Cleopatra is Egypt's sovereign. As long as her crown is secure, provided she preserves the supremacy of the Orient, and the commerce which fills her coffers with gold——"

A gesture from Antony cut him short. The shrewd diplomat realized that while arousing the Imperator it might not be bad policy to reassure the lover.

"Cleopatra loves you. Your precious body is more than all the world to her. But can she protect your power as we, your friends, can?—the defenders of your cause who have left everything to follow your standards? If this power is lost what will become of all of us? Ruined, hunted, condemned to flee from the vengeance of Octavius, what remains for us all but exile?"

The Imperator strode up and down his tent. He breathed heavily; his emotions seemed to choke him. Without having put them in actual words these truths perhaps had been already in his mind. Now, as they were laid definitely before him, he had a sudden desire to see clearly, even to the foundations of the situation.

"Speak!" he commanded. "What reason have you for thinking that the Queen has given up her ambition to reign with me in the Capitol at Rome?"

"The advice she is giving you!"

"You know what she advises?"

Dellius promptly recalled the number of times that the Queen had opposed their going forward to battle. Only a few days before at Corcyra, at Leucadia, when all the conditions were propitious, she had invented excuses for deferring action.

"It makes me believe that Cleopatra fears defeat less than she dreads a victory which would make you master of Rome!"

Antony made a signal for his officer to leave him. He needed to be alone. His tent, but feebly lighted by a smoking lamp, was very dim. He dropped on the couch, on which a lion's skin was spread. A storm was near. He felt the earth tremble, and rumbling thunder filled the air. It seemed as though everything most precious to him had received a sudden shock and were whirling around him. Could it be true that Cleopatra no longer coveted for him the rank of master of the world?

In reality Cleopatra had not ceased to desire victory for her lover, but she desired it in a manner which, as Dellius had pointed out, differed from that of the Romans. They, eager to return to their homes and enjoy the rewards that they felt they deserved, urged on the Imperator a war to the finish; she did all in her power to hold him back. Whether she had lost confidence in those warlike virtues that she herself had helped to weaken, and foresaw the possibility, if she risked all, of losing the heritage of her fathers; whether she dreaded that complete triumph which would lead Antony to Rome, she had given up her boundless ambitions and was now content with a policy of division. If the dominion of the Orient, commanded by Antony, were assured to her, she would cheerfully have abandoned Italy and its barbarous provinces, Gaul, Spain, and Mauritania, to Octavius and the Republic. Was this unexpected and complete change of purpose caprice or inconsistency?

To understand these vacillations, Cleopatra's career should be followed step by step from its beginning to the struggles which now racked her heart and soul. The young girl who was mistress of the middle-aged Cæsar had no thought but to use her powerful lover for her own best advantage; to obtain the security of her throne and the restoration of her sovereign rights. The meeting with Antony at Tarsus had made another woman of her. This bold son of Hercules roused all her passions and the axis of her life was out of place. Tender love-making replaced former ambitious desires. Jealousy and hatred entered into her soul and the peace of the world was in danger. If when with Antony she had kept the level head and wise reasoning of her youth; if she had let the conqueror of the Parthians carry out his ambitious plans, their interlaced names, instead of that of Octavius, might have been inscribed on the Pantheon of history.

But love had taken possession of her and its perpetual suspicions left her no peace. If Antony entered Rome as victor, what would become of her? And how could she combat that Aristocracy that hated her, as she had been able to do when she was sixteen? What Cæsar could not accomplish, how could this lover bring about? He was no longer young, and she knew that he was weak. These thoughts tormented her. In the midst of new and varied interests of his own would he still belong to her? Would he have the authority to impose her as Queen on his people; she, a foreigner, whom the voices of the gods and the people had alike rejected?

Her conduct can be traced to these fears. She

planned to keep Antony away from Italy; to oppose any decisive action, and gradually bring about a battle on the sea where, in case of defeat, there was always Egypt as a refuge.

Antony's friends were only too conscious of the difficulties which beset him. They had no longer that faith which, on the eve of battle, is a stimulus to those who are to go forth, perhaps to meet death. His generals, too, seeing him so absolutely under the control of the hated Egyptian, began to lose confidence in him. They wondered whether the two might not betray them. The idea of a conspiracy against him began to grow. Since their leader refused to uphold the sacred memory of Pharsalus, of Philippi; since he was being turned aside from the goal for which they had risked everything, let another take his place, let a true Roman take his place! And by common consent they offered it to Ahenobarbus.

Through anxiety and distress this noble soldier had fallen ill. When his comrades came to seek him they found him stretched on a hard couch of palm leaves which served him for a bed. His teeth were chattering with ague. At their first words he turned away his head.

"I will not listen to you."

"Have you no longer any faith in our victory?" asked Dellius.

The old soldier's heart gave a leap. He knew that the troops, heedless of the orders which restrained them, were eager to draw their swords. With him at their head what glory might be theirs? But to take command of the army meant betraying

Antony, his brother-in-arms, the close friend of his youth, the Imperator to whom he had sworn allegiance.

Dellius sat near him and reasoned with him:

"If you refuse, what will happen? The Egyptian will be our destruction. You cannot let us perish!"

With his burning hand Ahenobarbus grasped that of Dellius:

"Let me sleep now. I will give you an answer to-morrow."

Before dawn the next morning a ship set sail for Peloponnesus. Ahenobarbus left a letter on his table explaining the reason of his going. Everything around him was too distressing, too disturbing. In a question of remaining inactive, or of supplanting Antony as commander of the army, he preferred to retire.

This move was bitterly resented by his companions who had put their hopes in his leadership. All day they waited, thinking that he would regret his decision. When the sun set their eyes were still scanning the horizon. On the morrow, when it was certain that the best and worthiest among them would not come back, Dellius and Amyntas decided to join him.

When Antony heard that three of his generals had abandoned him, his brow was covered with icy sweat. His legs trembled; he leaned against the wall to keep from falling.

"The best of all," he whispered, and his eyes filled.

Before others he knew that he must control himself, and, to prevent their example being followed, he invented a tale to explain the departure. According to this falsehood, all three of these men were debauchees, who, unable to remain longer away from their mistresses, had gone to rejoin them. Other cases of desertion occurred, however. It was like an epidemic in which the poison spreads quickly.

After a scene with Cleopatra, who accused him of abusing her to Antony, Fortunius resolved to quit the nest of hate and intrigue which the headquarters had become. A boat, his baggage, everything was in readiness the following night when, before setting foot on the quay, the Senator was seized and put to death. Other executions followed and terror was widespread through the camp.

Antony was a changed man. He had completely lost his old, genial manner. The least annoyance upset him. A storm at sea served to convince him that all the vessels which had preceded him in the Gulf of Ambracia had gone to the bottom. A prey to a kind of vertigo, he was suspicious of his most devoted friends. He even accused Caius Sossius, the man who had given endless proofs of his friendship, of having delivered into the enemy's hands a detachment of troops in the passes of Epirus.

Like all his contemporaries, Antony had great faith in presentiments. They made an indelible impression on his mind. He saw the will of the gods revealed in them. He never failed to put on his right boot first; he kept silence in the dark; he always left a gathering if a mouse were heard; he never undertook anything without consulting the soothsayers, and only decided when they pronounced the comforting words: "Go, the blood of the victims speaks in your behalf." During the last summer that he spent at Athens, that summer of the year 31, when men's minds were seething like liquids in a vat, his statue, put up by the populace in his honour, had been overthrown in a thunderstorm. His terror was such that, while awaiting the doctors, his faithful Eros had to rub him vigorously with a strong ointment of warm oil and ammonia to revive him.

In the last days of the month of August his deep depression increased. As the inevitable day drew near, in place of the exhilaration, which formerly on the eve of battle had made him like a flashing god, he was sad, exhausted. It seemed as though all his muscular force had been suddenly taken away. For hours he sat motionless, as though the slightest movement would overwhelm him.

One morning, however, he came out of his torpor and went on board the *Antoniad* to review the fleet which lay in the Bay of Actium. It was there that Octavius, with his two hundred and fifty triremes with their curved prows, his hundred rapid despatch-boats, awaited him. Antony's fleet was much the larger. Well armed and equipped with formidable engines, it should have inspired him with confidence. He was cheered when his lieutenant, Alexas, called his attention to the good luck presaged by the swallows' nest in the rigging. His face lighted up; he jested.

"Before another moon the tiny galleys of Octavius will have fled before our ships, scattered like a pack of hounds."

At last his soldiers recognized their old leader. They gave him an ovation. But the next day other swallows flew in, killed the first and destroyed their young ones. And no sign brought such evil fortune as that!

Cleopatra, a true Greek, had the characteristic Grecian philosophy and did not share her lover's superstitions. To be convinced that she had taken all proper measures to insure success seemed more important to her than considering the blood of the victims! She had also that confidence in destiny which is natural to all beautiful women, who imagine that the gods, like men, will obey their wishes. Consequently she made her plans carefully, sure that they would succeed.

For several days the opposing armies had faced each other. Both sides hesitated. Confident in the equipment of Agrippa's fleet, Octavius wanted to force his enemy to a sea battle. Perplexed, uncertain, Antony could come to no decision. The sea was a new element for his war spirit; he had never won a victory on it, and his officers insisted that he should choose solid ground, the ground of Macedonia, rich in glorious memories.

The other influence, however, carried the day, for Cleopatra had so willed it. She knew that the results of a naval battle are rarely decisive and, in any event, retreat would be easier. It is not certain that she really preferred retreat to victory. Its results were hazardous, but the precautions taken showed that she was expecting it. If she did not, why had she arranged those relays between Greece and Egypt, why had she sent to places of safety the ships laden with gold and precious stones from which she was never separated? And why, above all, had she, on the very eve of battle, had the sails rolled up at the foot of the masts like sleeping sorceresses who would know how to wake themselves when the order for flight rang out? Thus all had been foreseen, prepared, made ready. She had only to be sure of that most uncertain and fragile of all things: the heart of a man.

The tie which bound Antony to his mistress, the fleshly bond that habit had, day by day, made stronger, was of the kind that rarely breaks. She had often had occasion to try its strength. In those latter days, especially, the necessity of having her beloved presence continually near him had become almost an obsession. The more uneasy and anxious he felt, the greater was his need of her. Nevertheless, Cleopatra was alarmed. It was never possible to know where the intoxication of victory, or the despair of a lost cause, might drag a leader. She knew that his will bent so easily that sometimes the giant became like a little child.

The night before the decisive day, the last day of August, which seemed in its splendour to have concentrated all the sunlight of the summer, the lovers spent the evening on board the *Antoniad*. Around them the brass-bound ships of the Egyptian squadron, like floating citadels with their stone towers, swung at anchor. Countless stars pricked the dark blue tent of night above them. For an endless moment they stood without exchanging a word. They heard the waves lapping against the side of the boat. It was a continuous sound, prolonged indefinitely, which seemed to express their thoughts before they had time to put them into words.

Antony sighed: "What will to-morrow bring forth?"

"Whatever happens, we have the invincible strength of being together."

Instinctively they grasped each other's hands in the darkness.

"Yes, our destinies are for ever bound together," Antony replied. Then, after a moment's hesitation: "If any disaster should occur, if either of us should . . . the projectiles will rain down . . ."

She had imagined many possible calamities, but not that a chance blow might kill her lover. At the suggestion, she shivered.

"Antony, my beloved, do you not know that I could not live without you? I have guarded against that horror. If you die, this dagger, hidden in my girdle, will quickly put an end to me!"

In an ecstasy of almost fanatic ardour he pressed her to his heart. He kissed her hair, her mouth.

"I love you, I love you," he repeated over and over again, as though the magic words could save her from harm.

"And if I am killed, what will you do?"

"Killed! You! But that is not possible. On the *Antoniad* you will be out of range of the battle!"

She looked at him dreamily.

"One never knows—we could be separated."

He could not imagine anything but death separating them. How could he live without his adored mistress, without her voice, her look? If she had her dagger ready, he had his sword!

She diverted him gently to less tragic possibilities.

"It is not only my death. One never knows what may happen to divide us."

But Antony was too wrought up to consider things calmly.

"Wherever you may be I will make a way to join you."

"You swear it?"

"I swear it!"

At last she had gained what she most desired. Let the worst come, they had exchanged vows, and she knew that at her signal her submissive lover would obey. Leave the rest to fate.

They listened silently, as though in the hope of catching some sign. Nothing, always nothing but the monotonous lapping of the waves against the keel. The stars began to grow dim. A rosy tint illumined the summit of the Othrys. Stirred by the first September breezes, the points of the great masts seemed to trace mysterious signs upon the sky. Dawn had come and the lovers must part.

"Good-bye, my beloved, until this evening," and they turned to their final preparations.

An hour later, as Antony was walking on the shore, he saw a centurion approaching, covered with scars.

"What can I do for you?" he asked, kindly.

"Oh, my Imperator, is it because you scorn us, our swords, our lances, that you are putting faith in those rotten planks?" said the man, pointing to the ships. "For the love of the gods leave the Egyptians and Phœnicians to paddle in water, since that is their vocation, and trust only in us, your old soldiers, who on solid ground will know how to conquer or to die!"

More moved than he cared to show, Antony put his hand on the brave soldier's shoulder and went on without reply.

It is said that at the very same hour Octavius met a man driving an ass, and asked his name.

"Fortune," answered the man, merrily, "and my beast is called Victory."

The coincidence is curious.

All possible suggestions and explanations have been offered concerning the battle of Actium. Nevertheless this famous day will always be an enigma, and the reason for the defeat will remain, for all time, a mystery.

It was about three o'clock in the afternoon. Since early morning the two fleets had been engaged in a fierce battle. As the bronze trumpets shook the roadstead, the galleys, like huge monsters, were rushing at each other. Missiles, arrows, balls of burning resin, whistled through the air. The steel prows of Octavius's fleet grazed the Egyptian mastodons. From their high towers these hurled showers of iron, which struck the enemy squarely. Both sides fought with equal ferocity and their blows were deadly. Limbs were scattered and heads fell, leaving only bloody masks in sight. No one could have predicted whose powerful machines would win, as they ruffled the surface of the water, a busy swarm that attacked, tormented, recoiled, and returned to the charge.

There was a sudden movement, an abrupt lunge, and the *Antoniad,* pushing her way through the surrounding ships, made for the open sea at full speed, followed by the royal squadron.

What incomprehensible motive had made the Queen act in this way? Why, with nothing as yet lost, or even compromised, had she given up the battle? Many have alleged that it was a deliberate plot with Antony. But why should they declare themselves defeated when they were not? No, Antony had no part in this premeditated flight. At first he was surprised, confounded. It could not be treason on Cleopatra's part! If from a variety of motives she did not want Antony to have the final victory, if she acted in a way to make it impossible, she surely did not wish Octavius to conquer? The avenger of Octavia, the representative of the Roman people from whom she had everything to fear? In the face of such astonishing contradictions the only answer is that human actions are not always logical, especially those of women!

From early morning Cleopatra had been watching the terrible battle. The unspeakable horrors had been too much for her overstrained nerves. For a moment the wing which protected her shifted. The danger of being surrounded, imprisoned, separated from Antony, threatened her. She was frightened. The assailants were very near, and her courage suddenly gave way. Standing on the bridge, like a frightened bird, she took her bearings. The wind blew from the north. It was favourable, and she took flight. Did she think of Antony and realize that in flying she condemned him? No, she remembered his promise to follow her, and her heart was comforted.

Unluckily she had divined only too well. At the first sight of the fleeing galleys Antony was puzzled. Was it a feint, a trap? Would their prows sweep around again and return to the battle more fiercely than ever? Then the truth flashed on him. His beloved was leaving him. Reason fled, and Cleopatra alone filled his heart and brain. Forgetting who he was and what was expected of him, losing all thought of those who were dying in his defence, he abandoned his post. A trireme was in waiting, all prepared for his flight, it is said. He threw himself on board and went after the woman who was leading him to ruin.

It was evening. A heavy silence weighed upon the sobbing waves. The *Antoniad* had stopped. At her stern Cleopatra was awaiting with palpitating heart the life or death issue of the day.

At last a light appeared and a boat approached. Antony came aboard; but no one would have recognized him. His head was bent and his shoulders seemed to carry the weight of the world. Without raising his eyes he crossed the bridge, followed by Eros, and reached the farther end of the ship. He dropped on a bench and buried his head in his hands. He felt as though he were at the bottom of an abyss. What had he done? What power, stronger than his will, had brought him there? For a soldier like himself to act as he had done! Was he a hero or a coward? A man with such triumphs behind him—and now he was praying for the darkness to hide him! What misfortune could be like his?

Cleopatra, leaning on the arms of Charmian and Iras to keep her from falling, watched him at a distance. He looked so morose that she did not dare to approach him. Was this the result of all her scheming? And then she saw the horrible blunder that she had committed in the name of love. If she had cared for Antony less, or loved him differently; if, from the outset of this unhappy campaign, she had only left him to follow his instincts as a warrior, he would not have been sitting there, a desperate man, his head bowed in shame! What a fool she had been! Why had she urged him to this battle against the will of all his counsellors? Why, above all, had she led this retreat . . . this flight, which she herself could not understand, so quick and irresistible had been her impulse? She asked herself whether, if she had had any doubt as to Antony's following her, she would have sailed away as she had done. And she knew that if she had not had the certainty that wherever Fate took her he would come, she would have had greater strength to carry on the struggle; that she would have been braver in the face of danger. She had slipped away because of her selfish confidence that in Egypt she would have him for ever. And now, before this broken-down man, who had no further feeling for her, all her wild folly was borne in on her. How could she imagine that Antony could live when his honour was gone from him? She turned her tear-stained face to Charmian.

"Do you think he can ever forgive me?"

Worn out with the horrors of the long day, the Greek girl was trembling. The carnage had frozen her blood. At the moment of the Queen's flight, although her terror was abated, she had felt that disaster, greater than any that had yet come, was close upon them. Now she could only say:

"Antony is a ruined man!"

Iras was younger and had more faith in the power of love.

"Go to him, Madame, see how he suffers! Your presence will comfort him!"

Cleopatra took two or three steps toward him, but Eros warned his master, and Antony, clinging to his despair as to a saving grace, shook his head as a sign that he wished to be left alone.

For three days and three nights he stayed there, without consolation. All his limbs seemed dead. He refused all food and was unconscious of the thirst that dried his tongue; but his mind was keenly awake to torture him.

His slave knew his humiliation of grief and said at last:

"Will you destroy the life that is so precious to us?"

"My life has no longer any value; glory was its only excuse for being. I am now like a man robbed and left naked by the roadside," replied Antony.

"But all is not lost; your friends . . ."

"I have no friends. Who stays by you in adversity? Foreseeing my defeat, no doubt those on whom I most counted have already deserted."

Crouching before the man whom he had always

looked on as a demigod, Eros embraced his knees.

"Others are faithful. I know those who would shed their last drop of blood to save you."

"Yes, you, my poor Eros, I know it well. But it is not your blood that I need now, but a promise."

Eros looked at him lovingly, submissively.

"Swear that the instant I command you to do it, you will deliver me from the curse of existence!"

Startled by these words, the slave jumped up, rebellious.

"I will never swear that."

Antony turned away.

"Go away and let me hear no more of your devotion!"

It was brutal treatment to the slave who had just offered his life and would have given it willingly. He protested, stifling a sob:

"My sword, my hands, my life, all are yours, my master. But as to the oath that you demand, if I tried to execute it, the hand that seized the weapon would, in spite of all that I could do, pierce my heart rather than yours!"

Left to herself, now burning, now shivering with fever, Cleopatra was forlorn. Was Antony going to die? Did he no longer love her? She went over in memory the days when, at the least sign from her, he was ready to crush her to his heart. How many messages she had written him in these last three days that he had not taken the trouble to open; and again she had the torturing thought that she herself had destroyed her own happiness.

But grief is not endless, and passion, however

shameful, is stronger than remorse. Days passed, and then Antony turned toward Cleopatra. They rested side by side, not daring to look into each other's eyes. The language of silence was sufficient. Words had no power to express their thoughts. There was no need to speak of their shattered hopes, to allude to that one fatal instant which had put them among the vanquished.

Deeper than their anguish, keener than the mortification to their pride, which had had no limits, was the intoxicating joy of being once more together. It wiped out all other feeling. It was irresistible, and their passionate love seemed all-sufficient, obliterating all other claims.

"Forgive me! I love you so!" his mistress pleaded, and Antony took her in his arms. Free for the moment from that remorse which was to poison all the rest of his life, he rested his head on the breast for which he had renounced the world. A kiss from Cleopatra was worth more than all the kingdoms of the earth!

X

The Death of Cleopatra

THEY were again in Alexandria. The people, deceived by the couriers that Cleopatra, for fear of an insurrection, despatched in advance, had welcomed them as returning conquerors. The city, from one end to the other, was hung with garlands; waving palms and arches of flowers made a triumphal way for them.

But this joy was short-lived. When the tragic collapse at Actium was made public the people were stupefied. The defeats on land were equally appalling. Each day fresh details of the downfall were brought in by the arriving vessels. Then came the news of the surrender, practically without a struggle, of the legions of Canidius; then of the Oriental commands, which, one by one, had withdrawn from the lost cause, and by bribery and treachery were seeking the good graces of their new master. Last came the tidings that Italy, as one body, had turned against her former idol, and with the fury of a trust betrayed, was clamouring for his death.

For the first few days Antony still kept some illusions. With the remains of his scattered troops he imagined he might be able to save, if not the vast empire which his former victories had created, at least the portions of it which belonged to Cleopatra. When he knew that his troops at Arcamia had fled; that the army at Cyrenaica, the best protected point in Egypt, had gone over to Octavius; when he heard of the treason of Alexas, his lieutenant, who owed everything to him, and also that of Herod, whom he had made King of the Jews and showered with gifts —he felt as though the end of the world had come. So these were the men he had trusted! In his prosperity he had seen only their flattering faces and had been blind to their possible perfidy. With such an outlook he gave way to overwhelming depression. He went over the past with vain self-reproach and accusations. And above all he condemned his over-confidence and his lack of recognition of his adversary's forces.

The thought of Cleopatra only aggravated his anguish and remorse. With that terrible clearness which follows disaster he beheld her as his blinded eyes had never before seen her. All the mistakes he had made at her command vanished like phantoms in the distance. To-day she was the one to rally quickly to retrieve their failure, to build anew their cherished plans.

Cleopatra was not a woman to be subdued. However weak she had been at the critical moment, the resources of her energy were boundless. Whenever she seemed in the lowest depths of misery unlooked-for strength enabled her to rise again. Her strong love of life compelled her, in the face of all misfortunes and disappointments, to look toward the future. In his despair this buoyancy irritated Antony. He could not understand it. Her attitude, in contrast to his own, exasperated him. Seeing her now as the sole cause of his downfall, he wanted to get away from her. Many times he prepared to leave her, but always her beautiful arms were about his neck and held him back.

One day, however, in one of their frequent controversies, she reproved him sharply for his inertia, and his old pride rose up. It was too much for him to have to submit to reproaches from her who had been his undoing. Since his ways no longer pleased her he would put a wall between them. An old tower of the Pharaohs stood on the edge of the river; in memory of Timon of Athens he called it his Timonium, and shut himself up there, with the intention of spending the rest of his life alone.

Accustomed as she was to his violent changes of temper, Cleopatra was not seriously alarmed. "Antony a morose hermit-philosopher; it is too absurd!" she cried, a smile of incredulity on her lips. "I will give him just two weeks to be back at my feet."

In the meantime what should she do? Her active imagination was busy. She thought that should ill fortune decree that the conqueror of Actium be one day the master of Egypt, she must find a way to escape him. The far-off Indies offered ideal conditions. Travellers to that country had brought back fascinating accounts of it. If she and Antony had to seek a refuge, why not find it in that land of enchantment, where delicious visions filled the air, where the perfume of the flowers induced blissful slumber, where the constellations of the heavens, surpassing in brilliancy Orion, the

Swan, and Cassiopeia, were reflected in the mirror-like waters? How was she to reach this magic land? It was useless to think of going by the Mediterranean and passing the Pillars of Hercules, which were guarded by Roman sentinels; but the Red Sea was there, then Gidda, then the Ganges! She need only move her fleet across the Isthmus of Suez and embark with all her treasures.

This romantic flight appealed to her adventurous spirit. She would not run the risk of being enslaved for lack of taking a short step. And she threw herself body and soul into this new enterprise. An army of workmen were sent to Pelusium. Enormous chariots, like those that formerly transported the stones of the Pyramids, were built, to be drawn by oxen.

Everything went on at great speed. Several ships had already crossed the sandy desert and were launched in the Gulf of Arabia when—she had not counted on this—agents of Octavius landed at Alexandria! Treason had done its work. All was destroyed, given over to pillage. What could not be carried off was cast to the bottom of the sea.

It was a cruel blow. Was she no longer to be that creature blest of the gods, before whom the elements yielded, like subjects to a queen? She had the feeling that henceforth, whatever she undertook, ill-fortune held her in its grip and would never loose its hold.

But it was not in her nature to yield. Since flight was impossible she would arrange for resistance. With redoubled energy she recruited fresh troops, equipped new ships, and negotiated alliances. Alexandria was fortified. In order to rouse the inhabitants to the defence of their city, she put Cæsarion's name on the list of the militia.

Cæsar's son was just eighteen years of age. Clad in his first armour, standing in his stirrups, this young man, who was meant to persuade rather than command, recalled the memory of his father.

In a clear voice he cried:

"Soldiers and citizens, your future king goes out to fight with you. Together we will use our swords against the usurper of Cæsar's name."

Applause broke out.

"Octavius shall not enter these gates," screamed a thousand voices that rang out like cymbals.

Cleopatra stepped out of her litter, from which she had been looking on at the scene. Many who had been applauding her son now prostrated themselves before her. Beautiful always, whether under the helmet that she wore in camp, or enveloped in the veil of Isis, she never failed to inspire admiration.

When he saw how much loyal devotion the Queen could still command, Antony was ashamed of his inaction. Besides, he could no longer stay away from her. Although his feeling for her was sometimes more like hate than love, she was necessary to him. One day, when his heart was heavier than usual, he realized how futile it was to try to endure life without her, and, full of repentance, he quitted his lonely retreat which had failed to bring him the coveted peace of mind.

Cleopatra was not surprised. She had known well that Antony, who in order to follow her had abandoned his post in battle, could not persist in his solitary confinement.

She welcomed him with open arms.

"Come to me! We have never needed each other as we do now!"

It was true; in their misfortune they had only each other. But their love had received a mortal wound. What each had done had placed an indelible shadow between them. Carried away by their violent natures they took up again the disputes and recriminations which had formerly forced them to separate.

Antony, especially, was incapable of hiding his rancour. At every turn he brought up the subject of the fatal day at Actium, which had marked him with dishonour like the brand of a red-hot iron. At other times their mutual sufferings drew these unhappy beings closer together. It made an indestructible bond. The hot breath of their guilt passed over them and they felt the irresistible need of uniting their forces.

They tried to go back to happier days and gather some of their old associates about them. With these old companions of their dissipations they formed a society, no less magnificent than The Inimitables, but with another name. This, which was called "Synapothanumenes"—inseparable in death —showed the state of mind of the two lovers. They had the same idea. They knew the god to whom their future libations would be consecrated. Their companions knew, also. Their feasts were as gorgeous as those of former days. They meant to rise above the common herd and show that they were determined not to endure a degrading lot, but to enjoy the days that remained to them.

Suicide was a virtue among the ancients; the final act imposed on them by misfortune. When life was no longer the distaff from which Clotho spun days of silk and gold, they gave it up, simply, as a useless thing. To put an end to himself Antony had the soldier's recourse, his sword, which, like that of Cato and of Brutus, was always at hand against the moment when he saw that the game was finally lost. Cleopatra's death would be more difficult. For those whose path through life has been strewn with flowers, whom youth still holds with magic arms, that last leap in the dark is a rude shock. To die was easy, but it must be done so that the accustomed harmony of life be not disturbed. How could she manage so that her lovely features, her fragrant body, should not be marred? As an artist who wanted to keep her place before the coming ages, pretending that her death had been a glorious one, Cleopatra had given much thought to this subject. She was prejudiced against using the ordinary poisons of the time. Perfectly familiar with the method employed to punish a conspirator, to get rid of an unworthy minister, or of an undesirable husband, she preferred the knife which left its deadly mark. The result of the usual poisons left her indifferent. What matter how many convulsions a dying enemy had? But for herself she wanted to study the matter carefully. She summoned Olympus, the celebrated physician.

He was versed in all branches of his art, having studied the effects of certain plants in Assyria, such as henbane and belladonna, which latter caused death or recovery, according to the strength of the dose.

In making her desire known to him the Queen said:

"Your fortune is made if you give me the means of quitting life painlessly and with no risk of spoiling my beauty."

Olympus was thoughtful. The Queen's demand was beyond his power; but he would do his best. He got together a group of physicians and they set to work. From the mysterious laboratory in a retired corner of the palace which had been set aside for them, red lights burned at night and sickly, bitter odours went up.

Experiments soon began. They were made on criminals who were condemned to punishment. The first results were terrifying. Forced to drink the deadly liquid, the unfortunate men writhed, their twisted limbs beat against the air, their distorted faces took on a greenish hue, and a hissing sound came from their dry throats. And this went on and on—prolonged indefinitely.

New combinations gave better results. The patients had a burning sensation, but the poison devoured them quickly and they fell, asphyxiated.

"Try again, again," commanded Cleopatra. "Your reward will be in proportion to your success."

One morning Olympus requested an audience. His eyes shone under his bushy brows. At last he had found the right thing.

Accompanied by the devoted attendants who had

sworn to die with her, Cleopatra went down into the bottom of the prison where the executions took place. She would judge with her own eyes.

A door opened and two colossal Egyptians entered, leading in chains a slave who had struck his master. He was a strong man and made a vigorous attempt to resist; but a funnel was placed in his upturned throat and the liquid ran down in spite of him. The effect was almost immediate; some convulsive starts, then a swoon. The man dropped between the arms that held him; he was dead.

A cold shiver ran over Cleopatra. Rapid as it had been, the scene left a horrible impression on her. Iras had not been able to stand it and was carried out fainting.

"Can you find nothing gentler?" asked Charmian, her face pale with fear.

"Not in the vegetable kingdom," said Olympus; "but there is the venom of serpents. You will see now."

At the same moment the door was opened to admit a young woman who had been condemned to death for killing her child. She was very beautiful and her tears made her all the more appealing. She fell at the Queen's feet, begging to be spared. The Ethiopians lifted her up.

"Have no fear," said Olympus. "You will feel no pain."

But she still implored pardon.

"Let me live, I want to live!" she cried.

There was a sudden silence. Without her knowing it the puncture had been made. Her lids closed, her limbs were heavy, she seemed asleep. Her heart had ceased to beat. Her face gradually relaxed, but lost none of its beauty.

Thus, painlessly, as though sleep had come, life had gone out. From that time Cleopatra was content. Her way of escape had been found. The conqueror of Actium would never carry her off alive.

But catastrophe was coming quickly. Pelusium had been captured and razed to the ground. Octavius's troops were camping under the walls of the Paraetonium. In this crisis what was to be done? Two hundred years before the days of knight-errantry Antony had a vision of knighthood. He would challenge his enemy to single combat. If he might only decide this mighty war in a tilting match and show the world, in full view of *his lady* and before the united armies, what a hero he was at heart!

Vain hope! When Octavius, without any risk whatever, had won the victory, why should he, coward that he was, expose himself to a fatal thrust?

"Go tell your master," he said to the officer who brought him the challenge, "that Antony can find several other ways to end his life!"

Before beginning the struggle which would settle Egypt's fate, and in spite of the humiliation of making any further request of a rival who had treated him so insolently, Antony tried, by generous self-sacrifice, to save Cleopatra's throne. If Octavius would promise to insure her sovereignty he offered to live near her, without arms, without titles, like an ordinary citizen.

Octavius did not even condescend to make any reply.

Several matters, however, were distracting his mind. Traitors and spies were not lacking in Alexandria and they reported that the Queen was experimenting with poisons and that, before her death, she had determined to set fire to her vast treasures. Now Octavius coveted these riches. The person of Cleopatra herself, which he regarded as the most brilliant trophy of his triumph, was scarcely more precious in his eyes. How was he to save these two treasures? Like the scheming man that he was, he consoled himself with the idea that all women, however arrogant when in power, are rarely so in adversity, and that undoubtedly terror, and the hope of gaining something from the present conditions, would make his beautiful enemy gracious. The main thing was to deceive her.

Consequently it was with her, and with her only, that he consented to enter into negotiations. He sent an ambassador to the Bruchium to represent him as inflexible; while, at the same time, Thyreus, a secret agent, slily, like all who do dirty work, intimated to the Queen that a reconcilation was by no means impossible. Fascinated by her charms, as all the great Roman leaders had been, Octavius wanted her to know that far from treating her cruelly he only asked the honour of serving her!

It is seldom that a woman fails to believe such flattery. Cleopatra, whose life had been a succession of conquests, to whom all the world had burned incense, was easily persuaded that she had a new worshipper. In spite of her experience of the world she might have been deceived by this mirage if one brutal condition had not accompanied the proposition. The demand was nothing less than the betrayal of Antony.

What Octavius really wanted was to get him out of the way. His great, humiliated rival annoyed him. A Roman general could not be chained to his chariot as Artabazes or Vercingetorix. Besides, with even a broken sword, his high-spirited enemy, defeated though he was, could dispute every inch of ground with him, and retard the final victory; and the Dictator was anxious to end his combat definitely and return to enjoy his triumph in Italy.

Unhappy Cleopatra! "How he must despise me to suggest such a bargain!" she groaned. Although her feeling for Antony was not what it once was; although the fugitive from Actium and the hermit of the Timonium had shown a weakness which was fatal to her woman's passion, yet she was indignant at the idea of such baseness. Too cunning not to take advantage of any possible chance of gain for herself, however, she took part in the exchange of trickery and, without refusing the proffered negotiations, asked time to consider them.

Spies, as has been said, infested the halls of the Bruchium, and one of them, the same, probably, who had brought word to Octavius, notified Antony that Octavius desired his death and that Cleopatra had promised to give him up to Thyreus.

At this news Antony had one of his outbursts of fury which swept over him like a hurricane. Betrayed! Sold by the woman for whom he had sacrificed everything! He thought of revenge. Should he slay her? He would rather put a dagger through his own heart. Should he kill himself? No, for his rival was waiting for her. Jealousy devoured him. Like his mighty ancestor, Hercules, he wore the shirt of Nessus and its poison tortured him. To love and to see in his beloved his bitterest enemy! His suspicions reached such a point that he would touch no dish until Cleopatra had tasted it, for fear of her poisoning him.

Justly indignant at such outrageous distrust, Cleopatra decided to inflict a lesson on the ingrate. It was toward the end of the supper. They were reclining side by side on the purple couch. She had amiably gratified the demands of the new order which required her to be served first. For a final libation she half emptied a cup of clear wine. A rose was in her hair. She drew it out, dipped it in the wine and, turning to Antony, said:

"Will you drink to our love in this cup?"

He agreed and put the cup to his lips.

With a quick motion she restrained him.

"Stop! See how silly your suspicions are. If I had any of the horrible intentions that you credit me with there are countless ways for me to carry them out. That flower was saturated with poison!"

Embarrassed, and not daring to meet her eyes, Antony fell at his mistress's feet. Would she forgive him? The little time he had left to live was not long enough to expiate the crime of which he had been guilty.

He prophesied better than he knew. There was only one day between him and the one when all would be settled. In that day, at least, he would accomplish wonders. It was the lion reawakening. The brilliancy of his warrior instinct would blaze out for the last time and show that, left to his own genius, he would have been a mighty hero.

The enemy's army was only a few furlongs from Alexandria. A hostile populace, on the point of treason, was not eager to defend it. The Imperator got some troops together, those who had been faithful to him through everything, and by a surprise attack, which there was no time to return, he fell on the cavalry of Octavius. Routed, pursued, the latter crossed the Nile in disorder and went back to the old intrenchments. For that day, at least, Alexandria was saved.

Drunk with a happiness that he had despaired of ever feeling again, Antony cried, "Victory, Victory," continually. Yes, for a last farewell Victory had come again and placed a crown on the forehead of the master who had won it so many times in vain. The old passionate love flamed in Cleopatra's heart, and her Antony was the magnificent, intrepid hero of former days. Seeing him in the distance, surrounded by banners, she left her window and ran down to welcome him.

In a transport of joy he leaped off his horse to press her to him, and these two, whom adversity had divided, were united again in the glory which was their native element. In the delight of being together all their past grief and bitterness were forgotten.

There was great rejoicing that evening in the old palace of the Lagidæ. The bravest soldier had a shower of gold. One of them was honoured by an antique golden armour, with the sparrow-hawk of the Ptolemys. The citterns and pipes resounded and the national songs were sung. It seemed like a revival of the days when the Imperator was distributing kingdoms.

Feeling that the hours were few and precious, the lovers grudged wasting any in sleep. It was a clear, mild night, when the soul is conscious of its own insignificance under the overwhelming vastness of the Oriental heavens. They wandered about the gardens until they reached the farther end, the place where Cleopatra had watched Antony disappear in the distance at their first parting. The rhythmic swell of the waters against the parapet sounded like their own heart-beats. To the right, the seven-storied beacon seemed to defy the stars; and above shone the crescent moon, whose silver reflections were like scattered petals in the sea.

This scene that they had so often looked on together carried them into the past. Standing there in silence, the exquisite joy of their former happiness was born anew, and tender memories of passing words, trifling incidents came back. They recalled those days at Tarsus, when in the first flush of youth they had embarked on their life-voyage with no thought of possible storms.

"Do you remember that first evening?" she whispered.

"Yes, your robe was clinging, iridescent, like the burnished breasts of doves."

There were other memories, hours of grief as well as joy; but they agreed that the most precious moments were those when they had each forgiven the other for some wrong. The present hour crowned them all. They felt as though they had traversed vast distances to find each other, and the certainty of faithful love from then until death obliterated all memory of rancour, suspicion, jealousy which had marred their life in the past. They were beginning a new existence here, surrounded by the bridal fragrance of the orange blossoms.

The wind arose. The sky changed from deep, tender blue to lead colour. A huge winding-sheet seemed suddenly spread over the face of the waters.

Trembling with terror, Cleopatra clung to Antony.

"Are you cold?" he said.

"Yes! No! I do not know. I feel as though darkness had entered into my soul!"

He smiled at her fancies. Although more easily discouraged than she, and more inclined to melancholy, he attached an exaggerated importance to the skirmish of the day before.

"Fear nothing," he cried, "I am strong again, and good fortune is ours once more!"

The words were scarcely out of his mouth when they heard a cawing above their heads. The crows were predicting evil things. It was Antony's turn to tremble. He looked at the horizon. The coming dawn revealed a monstrous fleet of ships crowded together opposite the channel. He recognized the same vessels which had faced him at Actium, and his quivering hand grasped Cleopatra's.

Pressed close together, like those who are terrified on a dark road at night, they retraced their way.

The steps showed white between the dark masses of the trees. They climbed up them slowly, as though weighed down by fatigue. On the last terrace they stopped. Never had the moment of leave-taking seemed so ominous. They were facing the fatal day. Their lips met.

"Good-bye."

"Good-bye"—and their voices died out in space.

The attack of the day before had put Octavius on his guard and he had passed a sleepless night. He had exhorted his men to take a firmer stand, reproached them for being put to flight by a few companies of soldiers.

"And that," he added, "at the very gates of Alexandria! At the moment when you were within reach of enough booty to have secured a home for every one of you!"

No further stimulus was needed. At the same time emissaries were sowing corruption in Antony's camp. They threatened to punish with reprisals from Rome the men who remained loyal to Antony; to the others they promised an amnesty.

Under these conditions the battle began.

Antony's new-born hope soon fell to the ground. In the very first attack the desertions began. Seized with panic, the brave men of yesterday became the fugitives of to-day; and among them, by a cruel irony of fate, he recognized the hero on whose shoulders Cleopatra had placed the golden armour. To have thought that he could move the world according to his wish, and to look on at this!

In despair Antony cast aside his buckler and exposed his bare breast to the blows. If a sword would only put an end to him! But the hour was not yet. The right to die is given only when the last effort has been made. And first, he must prevent a complete rout. Alone he undertook the titanic task. He was all over the field; on every side his wrathful gestures were seen. With the flat of his sword he threatened, he struck. His fierce voice resounded:

"Miserable traitors who change masters at a word!"

But his imprecations were not heard. The confusion was universal and the city fell quickly. Octavius passed the gates on horseback, all the legions following him.

There was one more chance: the fleet. But there, again, treason was rampant. The men stubbornly refused to fight. Oars in hand, they welcomed as comrades the men whom yesterday they had regarded as enemies.

All was lost. No heroic effort could have saved the day. Antony realized it and the roar of the blood in his ears deafened him. He went on like a demented man, surrounded by threatening fists and curses. Instinct led him to the Bruchium. The approach to it was in wild disorder. His heart stood still.

"The Queen! Where is the Queen?" he demanded.

An agonized silence was his answer. All the javelins of presentiment were at his heart.

"Cleopatra!" he cried loudly.

He was heard. An officer came from the royal

apartments. His face was sad. Before he could speak the lover understood.

"Dead?"

"Yes, with your name on her lips!"

At first the dread word had no meaning. Dead! She who filled the world. Dead! Had the daylight died, could heaven or earth die? Little by little the frightful truth dawned on him. He understood that he would see her no more. It was like a command given, as though he had heard the long-expected hour strike. He went back to his tent.

In these days of cowardice and treason Eros had never left his side. His brave arm had often warded off the blows aimed at the Imperator. Seeing him stagger at times, he had brought him reviving draughts. Now they were alone together. Antony controlled himself.

"Come, Eros, the time is here. The Queen has set the example. Draw your sword. Let me expiate the disgrace of a defeat."

The slave turned his head. His arm refused to obey.

"You promised me!"

"Master, do not ask the impossible. You whom I have just saved from the enemy's arrows! How can I?"

"Do you want to see me ruined, humiliated?"

No, Eros would not see that. He grasped his sword firmly, and spinning the blade so rapidly that it seemed to make an aureole around him, he hurled himself upon it with outstretched arms, and fell face downward, at the feet of his master.

Tears rolled down Antony's hollow cheeks.

"Brave Eros! You have shown me how to die," and he whirled his sword in like manner. The blow, unfortunately, had not the force of the one that killed his slave; Antony still breathed. He called, and the soldiers of his guard ran toward him.

"Strike," he commanded. "Stop my sufferings!"

But no one of them dared lay hands on that stately body from which such glory had shone.

But Cleopatra was not dead. On hearing that the army of Octavius, meeting no resistance, was marching on Alexandria her one idea was to save herself from the invader. The mausoleum where her treasures were gathered offered a safe refuge, and there she resolved to die.

But, once behind its iron grating, shut away from the living world, a cold chill ran over her. Was this the moment? Undoubtedly. There was nothing further to hope for. The last game had been played and lost. Servitude, captivity, with their threatening humiliation hung over her. Yet she hesitated. Why? The image of Antony was before her, vanquished, dishonoured, destroyed. Did she care to see him again? No, all was over between them. Their meeting place would be elsewhere, in those fields of asphodel that bloom in the land of shadows.

Why did she, who had so valiantly accustomed herself to the idea of dying, whose heart had nearly ceased beating, fall on Charmian's shoulder and cry bitterly? Her hand caressed the jade handle of the tiny dagger that she always carried, and she murmured, "I cannot!"

Was she thinking of breaking her promise? No, she would not survive her lover. She did not want to live. But, in the compact they had made, there was always the dread in the heart of each that the first one who went to the undiscovered country might not be followed. If she died, Antony, instead of joining her in death, might go to Octavia; and again her jealous soul imagined another of those reconciliations between them which had disturbed the peace of the world. She would take no chance of that. If she must go down into Hades at least she would be sure that her lover had gone before her, and so she sent him the false report of her death.

For the next hour the Queen suffered tortures in the depths of her mausoleum. How had Antony received the news of her death?

There was a sudden noise. A crowd gathered outside the walls. Cleopatra looked through one of the narrow openings which served as windows. Merciful gods! What was that the soldiers were carrying on a stretcher? It was Antony.

After he had wounded himself Antony heard that his beloved was still living and he wanted to see her once again. His arms were stretched out to her despairingly. How could he reach her? How get past the iron grating which protected the mausoleum?

And then a scene occurred, harrowing and barbaric, one of those superhuman acts which, viewed across the centuries, seems more fabulous than real. With the help of Charmian and Iras, Cleopatra threw down ropes from the roof and the wounded man was fastened to them. What a load for the frail arms of women! But, had it been heavier still they would have found strength to lift it up, for love made their muscles sturdy.

At last Antony was in his mistress's arms. She held him close and her burning tears fell over him.

"My lover! My hero! And I did not trust you!"

And Antony, heedless of his torn flesh that the least motion tortured, pressed close to her.

"Cleopatra! Beauty of the world! I am dying! Let me have your lips once more!"

She pressed him close. A few words, sobs, and the last breath went from him. Falling beside the lifeless form of him who had been her joy and pride, Cleopatra tore her breast.

"Most generous of men! This is where my love has brought you!"

When Octavius heard of Antony's death he was not overjoyed. His royal prey had escaped him. He must secure Cleopatra at once, before she came to herself and found strength to carry out her mysterious plans.

To gain entrance to the mausoleum was not easy. Proculeius, son-in-law of Mæcenas and, like him, blindly devoted to Octavius, undertook the task. He was an old friend of Antony's, one of those who, although they had gone over to the adverse camp, still retained a certain regard for him. Antony, when dying, had designated him as the only one whom Cleopatra might trust to defend her interests and those of her children.

Therefore, when he came, bearing the condolences of Octavius and of the Roman army, and asked the Queen to receive him, she could not refuse. Suspicious, as always, and determined to open the doors to no one, she tried to rise from her bed and go to receive her visitor in a lower hall, which communicated with the outside only by a grating.

But all caution was vain. While the deceitful messenger discussed, across the iron bars, the magnificent obsequies which Octavius was planning in honour of his great rival, his confederates effected a most cowardly entrance.

Cunningly as the plan was arranged, however, Cleopatra heard the noise. For a moment she did not answer her questioner. With anxious ears she listened to what was going on overhead. Then a door was flung open. Charmian came in.

"Horror! Treason! We are invaded!" she cried.

With ropes and cords the assassins that Proculeius had brought had scaled the walls. They burst in.

"Queen, you are a prisoner!" said one, as he approached her.

"Not while living!" cried Cleopatra, proudly, and drew from her girdle the tiny dagger which she had kept for such a moment.

Too late! The weapon was snatched from her hand!

Yes, Cleopatra was a prisoner. Through the lowered grating which she had sworn never to lift, she was led back to her palace between files of Roman soldiers.

Octavius was at last in possession of the long-coveted treasure. He was anxious to have an inventory made immediately. Preceded by slaves bearing flaming torches, he went through the subterranean vaults which Cleopatra had planned to burn. It was a world in itself. Marvellous works of art, priceless jewels, rare woods, rugs, were piled up to the vaulted ceilings. Many ships were needed to convey even the store of precious metals to Ostia. However phlegmatic this usurer's son might be, he could not restrain an exclamation of delight, which came from his heart, in passing through these stores of ingots, these piles of coins. These would put an end at last to the embarrassments which had plagued him since the indiscretions of his youth. All his debts would be paid. His legionaries would receive generous donations, over and above their just wages, that would attach them to him for life. With the stream of gold which would flow from this inexhaustible purse he could buy solid devotion. Was he not certain of wearing that imperial crown which Cæsar had barely lifted?

The people of Alexandria, who dreaded devastation and advocated a policy of prudence, welcomed the invader warmly. Exhausted by fifty years of revolutionary disturbances, they were only too willing to have a government that promised peace. The monarchial principle was, however, so deeply rooted in these servitors of the Lagidean dynasty that the surest way to obtain their respect and submission was to replace one crowned head by another.

The Imperator was no sooner seated on the throne than numerous well-wishers came to pay homage to him. Anxious to establish general friendly relations, he took care to flatter the pride that each Alexandrian cherished in regard to his beautiful city. Theatres, palaces, museums, temples above all—for he understood the importance of the priests' vote for the retention of the throne—were included in his carefully devised project. Concerned in all that could enrich his mind and help to forward the glory and magnificence of the reign of Augustus, he interested himself in the schools, the gymnasiums, the Library. He cultivated the learned men of the Serapeum, and was much gratified at meeting there the philosopher, Areus, who had been his professor at Athens. He promised to continue the independence which students had enjoyed under the former kings.

The visit to the Soma, that gigantic mausoleum, where the body of Alexander of Macedon lay in its crystal coffin, was of tremendous interest to a man whose only thought was glory. It is said that Cæsar, in the presence of the illustrious remains, had exclaimed: "I weep, because at my age this man had already conquered the world." His nephew, even more ambitious, examined the mummy long and carefully. He seemed to be questioning it, as though he were not satisfied with merely looking at the earthly form of him who had conceived and carried out such marvellous ambitions. He had the lid which covered the body raised, and, greedy to the point of profanation, he dared to handle the skull.

Cleopatra had been taken back to her apartments in the Bruchium. She was kept carefully out of sight of the people. Honours were not lacking; but these honours merely served to accentuate the fact that she was a captive, as they were all rendered by Roman functionaries. For fear of poison her clothes, her boxes, her person even, were continually searched. Her greatest trial was the continual presence of Epaphroditus, a eunuch of Octavius, who, according to instructions, played the part of courtier and under his obsequious manner concealed his rôle of jailor.

Emotion, disaster, grief, had finally broken Cleopatra's buoyant nature. That wound she had made in tearing her breast had become inflamed. Fever set in. The physicians pronounced the malady serious, possibly fatal. For an instant the unhappy woman believed that the merciful gods were going to save her from self-slaughter; and she gave herself up to the disease as to a generous current. So far from resisting it, she aided it, refused all medicine, and would take no nourishment.

Octavius was alarmed. Although he had obtained the treasure, he wanted the woman as well. He desired her perfect, not injured in any way. In all her beauty she would be the crowning glory of his triumphant return to Rome.

Trusting no one but himself to look after her health, which for that cruel reason was precious to him, he sent her word of his visit, thinking by this mark of respect to disarm his captive and deceive her as to his motives.

His calculations, at first, seemed successful. On hearing that the Imperator was coming to see her

Cleopatra improved somewhat. She decided to defer dying for the present! Before that irreparable deed she wished to see her enemy, to know what she was to hope or to fear from him.

Much has been written on the meeting of these two remarkable figures, who, after the manner of augurs, approached each other wearing masks. The object of the Imperator was definite. But what was *her* dream? What temptations assailed that mistress of the art of seduction to try her fatal powers once more? What hope did she have in those last days? That was the undiscoverable secret of a soul already on its way to eternity.

Those historians whose accounts of Augustus are full of adulation have described this scene as typical of the chaste and grave son of Theseus who was able to resist the seductions of the cursed courtesan. Perhaps, under other conditions, Cleopatra would still have kept this rôle of courtesan; but, at this time of infinite weariness, with her wounded breast, her tired eyes, her feet still trembling from having felt her throne crumble beneath them; after having buried the man whom she adored, and having in her mouth the bitter taste of emptiness, could she still have played the part of a coquette? Her keen intelligence, apart from her dignity, would have kept her from such a false step. With no intention of beguiling him, no hope of finding in him another Cæsar, or an Antony, she surely had the privilege of using what remained of her charms, scarred by thirty-eight years of passion and misfortune, to soften the heart of her captor. As to succeeding. . . ?

The two antagonists were face to face. Bowing courteously, Octavius took the chair near her bed that the Queen had pointed out. Then, as customary when greeting an invalid, he inquired as to her health.

With a sigh, she replied:

"You can see. I have no strength left."

Abruptly he broached the subject that was nearest his heart. Was it true that the Queen had given up in despair? That she would rather die than submit to his kindly rule?

She only sobbed.

He went on:

"Undoubtedly Thyreus has not delivered my message properly!"

She said that, on the contrary, she understood what a generous master he was and that she expected every consideration from him.

"Then be brave, Queen. Do not look on me as an enemy."

His voice was gentle, his expression kindly, but at a glance Cleopatra had comprehended. He was hard as a rock. He was trying to look human but she saw only the sharply cut nose that suggested a bird of prey, the dry, close-lipped mouth. No sincere words could come from it. She knew the part she must play. It would be a fencing match, and each must be on guard. She made a gesture of resignation.

"It is true; when Antony died I felt I could not go on living!"

"And now?"

"Oh! now I must think of my children. Dear

little souls! How can I leave them? At least I must know what their future in Rome will be!"

Her children! Cæsarion, Ptolemy, Antyllas, they were the first prizes that Octavius had seized. Defrauded of his principal victim, these innocent children would be sacrificed to their mother's insubordination.

The executioner went on with his hypocritical smile:

"Have no fear for them, Madame. Their fate is in your hands. If you put your faith in me and comply with my requests, no harm shall come to them."

She knew just how much this assurance was worth. She knew that the unhappy children would have to suffer; but she feigned confidence.

"I have the word of Octavius."

"And will you in return, beautiful Cleopatra, swear that you will not try to kill yourself? That you will not refuse to accompany me to Rome?"

In this frightful comedy, with a vain knave on one side, and the honour of a Queen on the other, who would win?

Cleopatra gave her word.

"You are my sovereign master," she replied, bending her beautiful head. "Wherever you choose to take me I will follow you submissively."

And to demonstrate that from that time on she was his vassal, she took from an attendant her list of jewels and handed it to Octavius.

"These are yours. I have only kept some ornaments, the most precious, it is true, in order to offer them myself to Livia, to Octavia."

This time he was really astonished.

"Do you really mean it?"

"Yes, I want your sister, who is sharing my grief, to pardon me for all the sorrow that I have brought on her."

However skilled he might have been in the art of deception, he was chiefly accustomed to dealing with men, and he did not understand Cleopatra's subtleties. Entirely confident that all would be well, he was about to leave her, but Cleopatra detained him. She had one favour to ask of him. As she was soon to go away from Egypt, to tear herself from the cherished city where her husband lay, might she be allowed to go to his tomb for the last time?

A docile captive, a generous prince! Following the example of Antony, who, after the battle of Philippi had so magnanimously honoured the bleeding body of Brutus, Octavius granted the request of his widow.

The next day, though hardly able to stand, Cleopatra was taken to the tomb. Her jailors accompanied her, which pleased her, as she wanted them to look on at the sad demonstration there. It was not enough to have convinced Octavius; she wanted it generally known that she had accepted her fate. Only in this way could she gain the liberty that she needed for her plans. She knelt down before an audience that would not fail to report her every gesture, every word. With tears and grief, which at least were not feigned, she poured on the tomb-stone oil and wine, the mystic nourishment of the dead. Her words came slowly, each cunningly conceived, and put together in a manner to deceive the world.

"Oh, Antony, my beloved! my hands that laid you to rest here were those of a free woman; to-day it is a slave who comes to offer you libations. Accept them, since they are the only honours, the last homage that I can ever render you. We, whom nothing could separate in life, are condemned to exchange our countries in death. You, a Roman, will rest here, while I, unhappy being that I am, will find my sepulchre in Italy, far from the land of my ancestors."

The effect of this pathetic farewell was just what Cleopatra had foreseen. The most skeptical were convinced of her sincerity. In speaking thus she surely accepted the decreed departure from the land of her fathers.

Epaphroditus, himself, astonished at the transformation that had taken place in the prisoner, was relieved to know that she had given up the thought of suicide. From that time on supervision was relaxed. The exits and entrances of the palace were unguarded. The Queen was allowed to entertain her visitors without witnesses.

A heroine who had borne so much suffering was worthy of profound devotion. What came to her exceeded her hopes. The man who would have risked his life, not to save that of the Queen, which, alas, was not to be saved, but to spare her humiliation, was a Roman officer. Young, handsome, of the noble family of Cornelius, Dolabella had served as staff-officer during Octavius's campaign in Egypt. Happy to have done with war, he was thoroughly enjoying the brilliant pleasures which the conquered city afforded.

One morning he was on duty as commander of the guard which protected the Queen's apartments. It was at the crisis of her illness. He saw her weeping, suffering, refusing all care. He heard her implore death to come as a divine mercy. Men usually prefer women who are happy, but turn instinctively away when they are suffering. Some rare natures, however, are drawn toward those who are in sorrow. When Dolabella saw the misery of this royal woman, whom the gods had first blessed above all others and then ruthlessly deprived of happiness, he felt a tender compassion for her. With a pity such as a neglected garden inspires he thought, "What is to be done? What help can I give? How can I aid this divine flower broken by the storm?"

Without having had any encouragement he approached the Queen, saying:

"Use me, Madame, as a thing that belongs to you."

It was a surprise to this sorrowing woman, whom all the world seemed to have forgotten. For a moment Cleopatra hesitated. Accustomed as she was to trickery and betrayal, she suspected some trap. He might be another Proculeius! But no, honesty was stamped on this man's face. His eyes inspired trust. Her bruised heart took courage and suddenly, with the faith of a young girl, she told him of the only one of her desires that had any chance of being granted: to know Octavius's intentions in regard to her, and to be duly warned of the day fixed for his return to Rome.

The young officer was in touch with the Imperator. It was easy to find out what his immediate plans were. Unconscious of being an accomplice to a fatal act, he agreed to do as she asked. It was a perilous promise which might have cost him his life. But even had he realized this he had been too often under fire to value life save for what it brings.

Three days later he gave her the information she desired. Octavius had decided to go back to Italy by way of Syria and Greece, and had given orders that Cleopatra, together with her younger children, be sent to Rome.

The hour had come at last. Cleopatra knew that henceforth there was no changing the fate which awaited her. It was time for the sword, which had been hanging over her for nearly a year, to fall. She regarded it fearlessly. Perhaps had she only drunk a few drops of bitterness she would have shrunk from the horror of it. But her cup of sorrow was empty; the game of life was lost. She gave the news to the two cherished friends, who had her full confidence, and instructed them to inform Olympus.

For fear of arousing suspicions, this manipulator of poisons had been kept in retirement; but his solicitude for Cleopatra made him vigilant and everything was prepared secretly. The Queen had no anxiety on the subject. She knew that at the appointed hour her means of freedom would be ready. There was nothing to do but wait and arrange things according to the carefully thought-out plan.

As a woman to whom elegance was a necessity, Cleopatra had determined to make her death, as she had made her life, a thing of beauty. Her queenly pride demanded that Octavius, Agrippa, Mæcenas, even Proculeius, all these Romans who had scoffed at her, should admire, not only the courage which had sustained her during the humiliating farce which they had forced upon her, but the envelope of her rare soul as well. With an ardour which left her quite calm she personally attended to all the little preparatory details of her toilet. As though she were making ready for meeting her lover, she bathed in warm, perfumed water. Her face was sweet with spikenard, and antimony gave a touch of mystery to her dark eyes. Her lips and cheeks were like burning roses. From the cedar chest came forth the snow-white robe, shining with pearls and gold, which had made her more than royal at the coronation feast. Some jewels put the finishing touch to her splendour.

What memories that brought back to her! The dazzling processions, the mad joy of the people, Antony, beautiful as Apollo, in his two-wheeled chariot drawn by the four white chargers; his stepping down and proclaiming her under the shining heavens Queen of kings, Empress, Goddess—and to-day, the winding-sheet!

As she fastened the amethyst buckle at her girdle Cleopatra's fingers trembled. But a stoic, she drew herself up. There must be no weakness. Her task was not yet completed. Instead of there being any suggestion of mourning here, all things should sing a chant of deliverance. Roses were scattered on the tables, on the carpet. Incense burned in the cressets. The shaded lamps gave a soft, rich light.

When everything was adjusted to harmonize with the great climax, Cleopatra drew a letter, written some days before, from a secret drawer. In it she had recommended her children to the generosity of the conqueror and begged him to allow her to rest by the side of Antony. She read it over, wrote the date (August 15, 30), the date that was to be her last day of life, and affixed the royal seal.

Was it as a jest that she charged Epaphroditus with the delivery of this letter? Perhaps, for Cleopatra had always loved to play with men or perhaps she merely wanted to get him out of the way. However that was, his ugly snout smelt some trickery. To go away from her seemed imprudent. He hesitated; but the message was important and the Queen persuaded him, with one of those smiles which no man could resist. The jailor yielded. Besides, why should he have any serious suspicions of a woman whose days were passed in futile occupations? Who since early morning had been poking in chests, turning over jewels and trinkets? Epaphroditus's shallow brain was incapable of comprehending the whims and caprices of a Cleopatra!

The evening repast was served as usual. The careless slaves came and went. That none of them should have any idea of what was coming, the Queen forced herself to eat and to keep up the conversation.

There was a sudden stirring behind the curtain. It sounded like a dispute. One of the guards came in. He could not get rid of a man, a peasant apparently, who insisted on speaking with the Queen.

"What does he want?"

"He wishes to give you a basket of figs."

"Let him come in."

Cleopatra understood. Her heart contracted violently. It required all her strong will to control its spasms. Under the peasant's garb she had recognized Olympus. Pale, but firm, she signalled him to approach. No word passed between them. They exchanged glances which made all clear. It was arranged. The gift had been paid for. She who received it understood what to do with it.

The Queen was alone with Iras and Charmian, those two devoted priestesses whose worship meant the immolation of themselves. These three women no longer cared to live and were ready for the sacrifice. No one knows, no one will ever know, what were those deadly rites.

The general belief is that an asp was hidden in the figs. Olympus had experimented with the venom of this serpent, which killed according to the conditions exacted by the Queen; quickly, without pain, leaving no disfiguring mark.

The idea of that age-old myth, bound up in religions for centuries, comes back. The woman and the serpent together. Their eyes meet, flames go out, they challenge each other. The serpent hesitates, draws back, then, enthralled by a look stronger than his own, darts, and in the willing flesh implants his deadly sting.

Iras died first. She was the frailest, and as soon as the poison began to circulate in her veins she bent down, rested her head on the knees of her beloved sovereign and held them till her last breath went.

Cleopatra felt her lids grow heavy. An irresistible langour overwhelmed her. Her mind began to wander and in her dream she saw Antony coming toward her to the sound of flutes and lyres. How quick and joyous his step was! They were on the sands of the shore. Where are they now? It is evening in a fragrant garden. A light breeze caresses them. There is music again, now it is fainter, all grows dim, then black. The eternal rest has come.

Charmian was still breathing when a clash of arms outside roused her. Fierce blows sounded on the door.

"Open! Open!"

The voices were commanding. It was a company sent from Octavius. He himself would be there in an instant.

The first words of the letter brought him by Epaphroditus had revealed the truth. The letter was a will.

"Run! Summon the physician!" commanded the Imperator. "Ten talents of gold to whoever will revive the Queen!"

But they came too late. The gods keep guard over those who resemble them. They had saved Cleopatra. Nothing could give her back to the hate of her enemies.

The first attendant to enter the room found her on her purple bed, which was upheld by the four sphinxes. All white, in the midst of flowers she seemed asleep. Her face had the serenity which comes from a duty fulfilled. With a reverent gesture, Charmian, staggering, with half closed eyes, was arranging her diadem.

"How fine that is!" railed Epaphroditus maliciously, furious that his watchfulness had been in vain.

"A superb pose, worthy of the daughter of many kings," the Athenian girl found strength to whisper. Then she fell near the Queen whom even to her last sigh she had adorned, served with a divine worship.

For Octavius it was a rude shock. He remained dazed, as though in dying Cleopatra had robbed his victory of its glory. What would Rome say? And Italy? The people, that pack of hounds who were devoured with impatience to avenge on the Egyptian all the humiliations she had inflicted on their country? He who to-morrow would be Cæsar Augustus had not forgotten his revenge. His captive had escaped him, but her children should suffer for her sins. Neither the prayers that she had addressed to him nor the pleading of these bleating lambs, whose only crime was in being born, could soften his infamous heart.

Antyllas was his first victim. Cæsarion's remarkable resemblance to his father, which seemed to make the divine Cæsar live again, should have preserved that innocent youth. On the contrary, it was another reason for getting rid of him.

"There is no room for two Cæsars in this world," declared Octavius, and gave orders that the young boy left in his care be put to death. As to the other children that Cleopatra had borne Antony, too young to be a serious menace, they were carried in the triumphal procession to take the place of their mother.

Only one of the requests of the dead woman found grace with the conqueror. He contented himself with her effigy and abandoned the body to the Alexandrians, who claimed it. With reverent care, arranged as though for her marriage, they placed, in the same porphyry sepulchre where Antony lay, the body of the woman whose passionate love had lost him an empire, but who in exchange had given him immortality.

THE END